Strong's

INDUSTRIES OF NORTH DEVON

Strong's
INDUSTRIES OF
NORTH DEVON

(1889)

A Reprint with an Introduction
and Notes by
B. D. Hughes

DAVID & CHARLES REPRINTS

ISBN 0 7153 5134 6

Industries of North Devon by H. W. Strong
orginally appeared as a series of articles in
the *North Devon Journal,* and was first
published in book form in 1889 by W. Michael, Barnstaple

Reprinted by the present publishers, with
the addition of an introduction and notes by
B. D. Hughes, in 1971

Printed in Great Britain by
Latimer Trend & Company Limited Whitstable
for David & Charles (Publishers) Limited
South Devon House   Newton Abbot
Devon

LIST OF ILLUSTRATIONS

facing page

CONTENTS

INTRODUCTION

THIS series of articles written for the *North Devon Journal* in the late 1880s has, as predicted at the time, proved of 'more than immediate interest'. Had Hugh Strong been able to foresee the present surge of interest in local history and industrial archaeology he could not have written a more enthralling set of articles describing some of the small manufacturing industries which flourished in the late nineteenth century.

Large industrial concerns have usually compiled a history of their particular trade, and as a rule they have kept documents and information which show their development. Similarly at the other end of the scale traditional rural crafts have been fairly well documented during their declining years. The small manufacturing industries, on the other hand, lacking the glamour of the heavy industries or the charm of the country workshop with its time honoured craft techniques, have for the most part gone unrecorded.

It is this then which makes *Industries of North Devon* a book of interest beyond the immediate area covered by the title. Small garment-factories, foundries and potteries, similar to the ones described, could have been found in almost every corner of Britain during the second half of the last century.

Perhaps it is fortunate that Strong's descriptions were quite unemotional, praising the factory owners for their initiative and drive rather than describing any shortcomings in the working conditions. Had he been more critical, I doubt whether these articles would ever have been printed in a newspaper which must have relied to some extent on the goodwill and advertising of these local industries. Strong himself points out

in his foreword that some industries had been omitted, through
no fault of the writer, but as a result of the scruples of the
manufacturers themselves. It is advisable then for those read-
ing these descriptions to use a certain amount of imagination in visualising what working conditions were like in the
industries described. The articles give us no information on
the pay or hours of work but, whenever possible, I have talked
to people who were employed in the industries at the beginning of this century and have included this information in my
notes on the articles.

Though information on small industries is scarce, contemporary photographs and drawings are even more difficult to
find. The camera was fairly common by the late 1880s but it
was still rather cumbersome and comparatively long exposure
times were still necessary in anything other than clear sun-
light. Consequently photographers, when they bothered to
take pictures of industrial concerns, concentrated on exterior
views rather than interiors. Professional photographers were
only called in on special occasions in order to record the opening of new buildings, the launching of ships, or works' outings.
Some of these faded photographs still remain on the walls of
offices or in the photograph albums of old employees, but each
year they diminish in number, consigned to the rubbish dump
or the bonfire. Wherever possible I have included contemporary illustrations, but in some cases where buildings, machines
or techniques had not altered, photographs of a later date
have been used. Some of the engravings are taken from the
Cyclopaedia of Useful Arts 1851, but though this is a much
earlier period than that dealt with in the book it is obvious
from the similarity between the engravings and the descriptions that the processes concerned had not changed appreciably
during the intervening years.

My notes on the various articles also include a very brief
description of the development or decline of the industries
during the past eighty years and in some cases an explanation

of processes or machines not described in the articles and now no longer in operation.

During the past half century the population of north Devon has declined rapidly especially in the villages. Attempts have recently been made to introduce new industries into the area. These include precision engineering, electronics firms, glass and plastics factories. Some of the older industries such as shipbuilding and the preparation of dairy products are, with the help of government grants, expanding rapidly, but the area still suffers from the same basic problem of poor communications that retarded growth during Strong's time. Until roads and railways are improved north Devon will tend to remain a delightful but economically troubled backwater, relying on preferential treatment to ensure industrial stability. The area still provides, however, a haven for those who tire of the turmoil of more prosperous regions.

NOTE: Even since these notes were compiled, several changes have taken place in the industries described.

The Pilton Glove Factory has finally closed down. The Derby Lace Factory has stopped the manufacture of machine made lace, though they still produce other materials. Appledore Shipbuilders have launched several ships from their new covered dry drock at Bidna Marsh and are considering a scheme to cover part of the old Richmond dock.

ACKNOWLEDGEMENTS

I would like to express my gratitude to the many people and organisations who assisted me in tracing information and photographs for this reprint. My especial thanks to Mr Simon Lloyd for his skill in photographing old and faded prints; Professor Walter Minchinton for his advice, and my wife for her encouragment and help.

May 1970.

Barry D. Hughes

Ordnance Survey grid references of industries described in this book. The one inch sheet No 163 has been used except where stated.

NOTES ON THE ARTICLES

ARTICLE 1   Barnstaple Foundry

Since the closure of Rafarel's Iron Foundry in about 1902 the foundry buildings on Newport Road have housed a cabinet-making factory and a small theatre. At present they are owned by Cox of Devon and used as garages, workshops and showrooms. The original buildings described by Strong have undergone considerable alterations during these changes, but the old foundry chimney stack stands in one corner of the garage forecourt, though unfortunately the ornamental railings which once surmounted it have gone.

Rafarel's Barnstaple Foundry was typical of the foundries and engineering workshops to be found in any medium sized town during the second half of the nineteenth century. They produced the many cast iron articles necessary to the building trade, ranging from drain pipes and man-hole covers to kitchen stoves and boilers. Many of the items specially produced for local councils such as park benches, lamp standards and horse troughs were extremely complex castings decorated in the lavish Victorian manner, with flowers, leaves and fruit.

At the time of Strong's article there were three foundries in Barnstaple catering for the agricultural implement industry, the shipbuilding industry and also producing waterwheels, pulley wheels and gearing for local millwrights.

When the foundry closed the premises were taken over by the Barnstaple Cabinet Company who incidentally made the patterns and shuttering used in the construction of some experimental concrete ships built at Barnstaple during World

War I. The part of the property facing Newport Road was converted during this period into the John Gay Theatre which flourished until the late 1930s as a repertory theatre and summer music hall.

There are still plenty of cast iron articles in Barnstaple and District which bear the inscription 'Rafarels Iron Foundry', but with improvements to street lighting, road works and property restoration these get fewer each year. One place where the name can still be seen is on the cast iron pillars which hold up the roof of the present garage workshops. The large workshops at the back of the property once housed the main casting shop where the iron pilasters of the Taw railway bridge were cast.

ARTICLE II   THE DERBY LACE FACTORY

Apart from a short period during the depression of the late 1920s the lace factory at Barnstaple has been in operation for over 145 years. In 1927 Miller Bros, the owners of the factory at the time of Strong's description, sold the premises to a firm of spinners who managed to operate for about eleven months before being forced to close due to lack of work. The present owners, T. C. Small & Tidman, took over the factory in 1929.

Most of the tightly packed houses which surrounded the factory until ten years ago, have been demolished to make room for car parks and an estate for elderly people. This gives a clear view of the old four storey main factory building which has recently been painted. The building when viewed from the main gate is quite well proportioned and proves that some old factories need not be eyesores if properly maintained.

The large red-brick building opposite the factory was once the evening institute, started in 1900 by Miller Bros for their workers. In 1934 this building was taken over by Devon Education Committee and is now occupied by the Barnstaple

Boys County Secondary School.

The appearance of the factory from the main gate has not changed much since Strong described it in 1889. Most of the alterations have taken place at the rear of the old buildings where large new workrooms have been built to accommodate the modern machinery.

The blacksmiths' shop, pattern-making shop and part of the engineering workshops have also been demolished to make way for new workrooms and a despatch bay. As the factory no longer makes its own machinery, the engineering workshops are now only required to repair and maintain equipment.

The fundamental processes involved in the mechanical manufacture of lace net have not altered since Heathcoat's Patent of 1808. The looms are now powerdriven and much wider, and the materials are mainly man-made fibres, but the basic principles on which the machines work remain the same. Net-making machines designed and built at the factory in the last part of the nineteenth century have proved so efficient that they can still keep pace with their modern counterparts. One of the plain net machines still in use at the factory first went into production on the 28 September 1876 and is still in first class condition.

One of the factory's oldest employees started work there in 1915, as a girl threader, aged thirteen. She recalls that in those days the workers employed a 'knocker up' to go round the town and rouse them in good time for starting work at 6am each morning when the large bell on the roof of the main building was rung. There were fines if workers were late. At 8.30am there was an hour's break for breakfast, followed at 12.30 by a one-hour break for lunch. During the afternoon a fifteen minute tea break was allowed at four o'clock. The day's work ended at six o'clock. These were considered good hours at the time. Starting pay was seven shillings a week with a rise of sixpence a week after each six months of employment. Many workers went to the institute in the evenings for further education, as most had left school before the age of fourteen.

ARTICLE III   PILTON GLOVE FACTORY

Only two workrooms at the top of the Pilton Glove Factory are in use today. In these two light and airy rooms the dozen or so remaining cutters still shape the various parts for leather gloves with the same type of hand shears used in Strong's day. The parts are then sent to Shepton Mallet where they are made up into finished gloves at the factory of Dent & Allcroft, the Pilton firm's present owners. All the machinery has been removed from the factory, but the buildings remain almost unaltered except for the removal in 1937 of the leather-drying kilns. They were demolished to make space for new workrooms, but some of the old beams and hooks used for hanging the skins can still be found in the derelict out-buildings. The field at the back of the factory where the leather and, in earlier times, woollen cloth was once stretched and dried is still known as 'rack field', though it is now a market garden.

As recently as 1937 glove making was still an important industry in Barnstaple. At that time Dent & Allcroft had two factories in the town employing over 350 people, plus an equal number of outworkers. Now only the few workers at Pilton remain, though leather gloves are still made at Bideford, Torrington, and Appledore.

The main reason for the decline of the industry appears to be a change in fashion, mainly brought about by improvements in transport facilities. Today the necessity of walking has been cut to a minimum and as travellers we are now provided with shelter and warmth. One has only to ride a horse or bicycle in wet or cold weather to realise how desirable a good pair of leather gloves must have been in the days before enclosed motor vehicles became as common as they are today.

ARTICLE IV   BARUM WARE POTTERY

The exterior of the Barnstaple Ware Pottery of C. H. Brannam Ltd in Litchden Street, Barnstaple is virtually the same as when Strong described it in 1889.

The firm, which became a limited company in 1914, still produces items of traditional Devonshire pottery such as pitchers, jugs and bread pans together with many kinds of mugs, plates, bowls and vases. They also produce several million flowerpots each year in all sizes from over a foot in diameter to just over an inch, but they no longer make drain pipes, bricks or tiles.

Most of the machinery is now driven by electricity including the pug mill and the potters wheels. Electric kilns have also been installed to speed up production of the smaller and more delicate items made in the pottery. The two large coal-fired bottle kilns which tower over the workshops at the back of the pottery are now mainly used for the larger items such as garden vases, pickling jars and flowerpots. As these kilns may not be in use for very much longer, I have included a photograph and some notes on them.

Three men are permanently employed in looking after the two kilns. It takes them two days to fill one of the kilns with its load of 15 tons of pottery and 15 tons of kiln furniture, saggers, etc. The firing takes between 48 and 50 hours, during which time $4\frac{1}{2}$ tons to 5 tons of coal are used. The kiln is usually lit at 5pm and the workman who starts the firing then tends the kiln until 6am the following day. The second man takes over to look after the firing until 7am the next day, a shift of 25 hours. The kiln is then left to cool down under the supervision of the third member of the team. During this time the second kiln will have been emptied and prepared for its next load of pots.

Brannam's still mine their own clay at Fremington from the same pits which were used by Fishley's Fremington Pottery

(Chapter XII). During the summer the firm welcomes visitors who wish to look round the pottery.

ARTICLE V   ROLLE'S QUAY STEAM MILLS

Messrs Rawle, Gammon & Baker and their partner companies Rock Trading and RGB Paints still occupy their original site by the Braunton Road Bridge, Barnstaple. As Strong predicted, the firm has grown considerably. The yard has now been raised above flood level and large timber stores and showrooms have been added, though the offices are still in the original brick buildings.

In 1932 a branch of the firm opened in Bideford. As with the Barnstaple site the land was low-lying and liable to flooding during high spring tides. Between 1940 and 1945 the showrooms and stores at Bideford were used as a factory for aeroplane parts. During this period a large timber-drying kiln was erected for the seasoning of timber used in the aircraft industry.

Strong refers in his description of the Barnstaple yard to the 'old saw pit'; this was a long trench about 7ft deep over which logs were placed for conversion into planks. Until comparatively recent years this was the standard method of cutting up logs in many local industries, including shipbuilding, wheelwrighting and the building industry. Though ready-sawn Baltic timber has been imported since the later half of the nineteenth century there are still plenty of people in north Devon who have worked in saw pits; none of them are sorry that this arduous and unpleasant work has now been taken over by machinery. As this method of converting timber has now completely disappeared I have added these notes to show how it was done.

The sawyers were usually specialists in the work. They worked in pairs known as the top sawyer and the pit man. The log to be converted would first be rolled onto strong bearers placed across the top of the pit or raised up onto a heavy timber framework which supported the log above the ground. This was the case where the pit was liable to flooding. The lines for the saw cuts were marked by stretching a chalked or blackened string along the log then snapping it against the surface to leave a straight line.

The top sawyer then climbed onto the log whilst the pitman descended into the pit. The saw, a massive object with a blade 7ft long surmounted by a T-shaped handle, was then placed at the end of the marked line. In the pit the bottom sawyer clamped his handle onto the blade. The saw teeth were arranged so that they cut on the downward stroke, the top sawyer then had to pull the blade back up and also keep it on the line. One of the tricks of sawing was to bring the blade down in a curving motion on the cutting stroke; if this was not done properly the pitman was very soon worn out. As the cut progressed, the bearers on which the log was supported had to be moved. In order to do this the pit man's saw handle was removed and the saw withdrawn from the cut. Saws had to be carefully sharpened at regular intervals depending on the type of timber being cut. This was the job of the top sawyer. During those intervals the pitman would retire to the nearest pub to quench his thirst, with the inevitable consequence that the top sawyer would have to go and fetch him when he was ready to stark work again and would, of course, take some refreshment at the same time. The fact that sawing was such thirsty work tended to give these men a bad reputation for drunkenness, though most of the old tales about them emphasise their remarkably accurate work.

The raft of timber mentioned in the chapter as having caused havoc at sea probably referred to an attempt in the 1850s to float a timber raft across the Atlantic. The practice of floating rafts of timber up the river Taw from ships moored in Appledore Pool was abandoned in the 1860s as many logs went astray on this short journey; river barges were used instead. The photograph of Rolle Quay taken in 1895 shows some of these barges unloading timber for Rawle, Gammon & Baker.

During the past eighty years the firm has built up a large sales and distribution network dealing in all branches of the building industry. They now have their own gravel barges, cranes and a large fleet of lorries serving all parts of Devon. In 1970 the firm celebrated its 120th anniversary.

BRADIFORD TURNING MILLS

The ruins of the Bradiford Mill can be found by the side of the stream about one hundred yards below Bradiford Bridge. The general layout of the site is still clear, though the roof on some of the buildings was destroyed in the fire which closed the factory in 1935. The leat which once supplied water for the mill flows on one side of the buildings and the Bradiford Stream on the other, making part of the site virtually an island.

The waterwheel pit is still visible, and though the wheel has been removed, the sluice which controlled the flow of water to the wheel remains. On the sluice is cast the name of the millwrights. 'Garnish & Lemon Barnstaple'. This firm, which had its workshops at the bottom of Pilton Street, Pilton, Barnstaple, made most of the machinery and equipment for local watermills.

Strong mentions that the mill was once used as a tucking or fulling mill. These mills, once common in Devon, were employed in cleansing grease and superflous oil from the woollen cloth manufactured in the district. The scouring was achieved by the action of large wooden mallets pounding the cloth in a trough containing a mixture of water and fullers earth. Power to raise the heavy mallets was supplied by waterwheels. North Devon cloth was made mainly from short fibred wool which had to have an extra pounding or milling in order to cause maximum shrinkage and so mat together any loose fibres in the material.

When in operation the brush mill employed about half a dozen men. The wages of a turner at the mill just after World War I were in the region of £1 for a 60-hour week, a low wage even in those days, but comparable with that of a journeyman potter in the local potteries at the time.

ARTICLE VI   VINCENT & DUNCAN'S
                 COLLAR FACTORY

The buildings which once housed the factory are still standing at Westcombe, Bideford, though they have been divided up and used for a variety of purposes in the past fifty years. The block of buildings facing Westcombe Road served as the offices of the Bideford Labour Exchange for many years until new offices were opened in North Road. Other parts of this block are used by the local council as a depot and stores.

The south wing, including the old mill building, has been taken over by a coal merchant for offices and stores. The oldest and most interesting part of the building was originally a flour mill which took its power from a small stream (now underground), which runs down the coombe. This stream runs very low in summer, and the mill must have suffered through lack of water. At some time a steam engine was installed (hence the chimney which was mentioned in the chapter, and has since been demolished). Even this form of power failed to solve the problems of competing with the larger steam mills which sprang up during the middle of the last century. These highly mechanised mills imported bulk cargoes of foreign grain and could therefore sell flour at a much lower price than the small town millers who ground mainly home grown cereals. As a result of this competition and a general decline in cereal

growing in this part of Britain, many Westcountry mills fell
into disuse. The mill buildings provided suitable premises
for small clothing-manufacturers who were at that time moving away from the centres of industrial unrest in search of
new sources of cheap labour.

The growth and prosperity of the factory was obviously due
to the fashion of wearing high starched collars and loose
starched cuffs. White-collar workers were on the increase and
by 1900 the *Tailor & Cutter* was commenting on the new 3in
high collars that were 'certainly more than the average man
can wear with comfort'. But the fashion persisted and even as
late as 1909 one could purchase 2¾in Baden Powell collars for
4½d each.

The end of World War I saw a return to a more informal
mode of dress. Together with the general depression in trade,
this led to the closure of the factory in about 1925.

The 'Otto' gas engine which powered the factory was
typical of the motive power of many small industries towards
the turn of the century. Steam engines were expensive to
install and required the constant attention of a boilerman. On
the other hand the gas engine, first produced by Crosleys of
Manchester in 1876 under the patent of N. A. Otto, could be
started in the morning and left to run all day with little or no
attention. They were simple to install, cheap, clean and had
no need of a chimney stack, coal store or boiler, thus saving
considerable space and capital.

They ran on a mixture of coal-gas and air. This mixture
was drawn into the cylinder, compressed, then ignited in a
heated tube, or later by an electric spark. The explosion provided the power stroke; a large flywheel then drove the piston
back up the cylinder expelling the exhaust fumes and pulled
it back down the cylinder to draw in a fresh mixture of gas
and air. These engines were the forerunners of the modern
internal combustion engines which have not only revolutionised transport but have provided power and lighting for farms

and small workshops not served by mains electricity. By the turn of the century the Appledore Factory had also been provided with one of these engines.

ARTICLE VII   VAUGHANS GLOVE FACTORY
TORRINGTON

Vaughans Glove Factory, which as Strong points out looks like a chapel, continues to produce all kinds of fabric gloves. It is now under the direction of Mr Vincent, grandson of G. W. Vincent, one of the partners in the Bideford Collar Factory, described in Article VI. The layout of the workshops is much the same as described eighty years ago. Only the box-making department, which became uneconomical, has been dispensed with. Some of the old screw presses used in the cutting of the glove fabric are still in operation on the second floor, but they have been replaced to a large extent by modern electrical presses. Most of the sewing machines are now driven by electricity and only the most delicate work is still done on traditional treadle machines. Part of the overhead line shafting which used to drive the machines still remains but the oil engine which drove it was scrapped in the late 1950s. Ironing or puffing the gloves is now done on electrically heated metal hands, similar in appearance to the old steam-heated ones described in this chapter.

Employment at the factory has declined over the years but some of the processes are still undertaken by outworkers living in the villages around Torrington.

Vaughans continue to export fashion gloves to all parts of the world. They have also added specialised industrial gloves, such as those used by assembly workers in the electronics industry, to their list of products.

The front of the factory is decorated by two relief carvings in stone. One shows a pair of gloves, the other depicts one of the old screw presses. These carvings will probably remain as a reminder of Torrington's association with the glove industry long after the industry itself has ceased to exist.

ARTICLE VIII — APPLEDORE SHIPYARD

In the past the shipbuilding industry has tended to act as a barometer of trade. During times of prosperity it booms, new ships are built and old ones kept in good repair, but as soon as there is any sign of a trade depression, orders for new ships cease and old ships are laid up. Shipbuilding on the rivers Taw and Torridge has suffered the consequences of these fluctuations for several centuries.

At the time of Strong's visit to the yards, Appledore had not changed over to the building of iron ships as the first steel schooners were built in 1890 at Middle dock, now Fulford's storehouses and quay. The yards, therefore, were well equipped and eager to cater for the repair and maintenance of the large but rapidly diminishing number of wooden sailing ships.

Of the three yards described by Strong, Richmond yard and Newquay yard are now under one management. The third, Churchfield yard, was on the site of the present Seagate Hotel car park. The slipways of this yard were covered over when Appledore quay was extended. The sailmaking lofts and some of the workshops have since been converted into houses.

The Cock brothers who ran Churchfield and Richmond yards, later undertook the construction of iron and steel ships at what came to be known as the Iron yard, situated between the Newquay and Richmond yards. In the late 1890s Westacotts moved to the shipyard at Lower Cleavehouses, Bideford. Newquay yard was taken over by the firm of P. K. Harris which later acquired Richmond yard and the Iron yard.

They continued to build and repair all types of coasters and harbour craft both in wood and metal. The last wooden merchant schooner to be built in Appledore, the *P. I. Harris,* was launched from their Hubbastone yard in 1912.

During the first and second world wars Harris built minesweepers, torpedo boats, gun boats and harbour craft of all types for the Admiralty, returning in peacetime to the building of tugs, dredgers and small coasters. One unusual contract was gained in 1961 when they built the ice breaker, *Perkvn* for the Polish Government.

In 1958 the firm of Seaworks Ltd took over control of P. K. Harris' shipyard. When, in 1963, Seaworks went into liquidation the outlook for Appledore was bleak as most of the population depend on the shipyard for their employment. Fortunately the yards were kept running by a group of local businessmen under the name of Appledore Shipbuilders. In 1965 this firm came under the control of Court Line Ltd, their present owners. During the last five years the yards have been modernised and a new dry dock has been constructed at Bidna Marsh, where ships of up to 380ft can be built under cover.

Appledore Shipbuilders specialise in the construction of relatively small but complex craft, such as ocean-going and harbour tugs, trawlers, small tankers, service vessels, and dredgers. These ships call for a high concentration of specialised machinery, pumps, freezing plant, deck equipment, etc, in a limited hull space. In the past few years they have built up a reputation for skilled workmanship and prompt delivery.

As shipbuilding in Appledore has changed considerably since 1889 and will probably change as much in the next half century I include a brief description of the yards as they are today.

The layout of the Richmond and Newquay yards is similar to what it was at the turn of the century. The large dry dock at Richmond yard, built in 1855 by William Yeo for the building and repairing of schooners engaged in the Newfoundland cod trade, is still in use. This dock, originally intended to take up to four schooners at a time, is now used for building steel ships of up to 312ft in length. A Goliath travelling crane now spans the dock to facilitate the installation of engines and heavy machinery, a job which previously had to be done after launching by the 30 ton luffing crane at Newquay yard.

Richmond yard has two other building berths, with slipways into the river; each is capable of taking craft up to 190ft in length. Between the dry dock and the slipway is a large workshop which houses the mould loft where full sized patterns are made from the ships plans. These are then taken to the ground floor of the workshop where steel sheets are marked out and cut to the shape of the patterns. Various parts of the ship, such as bulkheads, frames and deck houses, are subassembled in this workshop then taken out to the building berths or dry dock where they are incorporated in the final assembly of the ship.

The rolling and forming of shell plates, frame and beam bending is done at the anglesmiths' shop at the top of the slipway. Next to this is the plumbers' shop which deals with the complex piping systems found in modern ships. The fitters who supervise the installation of the engines, shafting, rudders and all auxiliary machinery also have a workshop in this area.

Newquay or Top yard is separated from Richmond yard by about four hundred yards of narrow twisting road. Here the firm has its administrative block which also houses the design and drawing offices. This yard is mainly engaged in the fitting-out of vessels, that is the installation of machinery, electrical equipment and accommodation. When vessels leave the top yard they are complete in all respects and ready for sea. Newquay yard has its own stores, fitting, plumbing, electrical and paint shops and also a dry dock capable of taking vessels up to 165ft in length. Part of this old dry dock was filled in about a year ago. Originally it had a bend in the middle rather like a boomerang. This was because the site could not accommodate one long straight dock. It was intended to take two or more small ships at a time and not, as the workmen have convinced one or two visitors in the past, for the building of banana boats. Ships and barges of up to 150ft in length have also been built on the quayside at this yard and launched sideways into the river at high tide.

At present the company employs about 500 men, but with the expansion programme at Bidna Marsh this will probably rise to about 800 in the next few years. In order to train apprentices and keep pace with the latest developments in shipbuilding, the firm has opened its own training centre at Bideford.

ARTICLE IX   DEVON ART POTTERY

Nothing now remains of Lauder & Smith's pottery and brick works on Pottington Marsh, Barnstaple. The works closed some time between 1900 and 1904 and the site, between Rolle Street and Pottington Road, has since been used for housing.

ARTICLE X   TORRIDGE VALE DAIRY
TORRINGTON

The factory has grown considerably since 1889 and is now one of the largest in Europe. The works cover an area of about 5 acres near Taddiport in the valley below Torrington. Apart from the closing of the market gardening side of the business in 1919, the factory continued to operate in much the same way as described by Strong until about 1922. Then Robert Sandford, the founder of the firm, went into partnership with William Stacey and two years later he retired and Stacey was joined by Thomas Richard Sandford. The factory was enlarged by the new partners and in 1932 became associated with Messrs Cow & Gate Ltd (later Unigate), though local organisation continued mainly under the direction of Sandford

& Stacey until 1958.

By 1948 a much larger factory had been built which incorporated all the latest milk-processing machinery, including what was then one of the world's largest milk-drying machines. The new factory had its own water purification plant installed to cope with the large volume of water required in dairy processes.

In 1948 when milk was collected from farms all over north Devon as far apart as Lynton in the east to Camelford in the west and Okehampton in the south, production had reached over 48,000 gallons per day.

Between 1967 and 1969 the factory was enlarged again and though the collection area is smaller, both milk and butter production have grown. The throughput in 1970 is in the region of 160,000 gallons per day and the factory now employs 350 people including lorry drivers. technicians and laboratory workers.

Together with the Dartington glass factory and the plastics factory the dairy has taken the place of many of the older industries of Torrington such as tanning and glove-making.

The Rolle road mentioned in the chapter was a toll road laid over the bed of the old Rolle canal when it closed in 1871. Never popular with the trades people of Torrington as it bypassed the town, the road is now used as a footpath alongside the river.

'STAR' PLOUGH WORKS

The 'Star' Agricultural Engineering Co Ltd is still trading in South Molton. The firm no longer manufactures agricultural machinery but is concerned mainly with the sale and repair of agricultural equipment. ' Dicky ' Bawden, the inventor of the plough described in Chapter X, left the 'Star' Co in 1901 and set up his own works in South Street, South Molton.

He is reputed to have been the first man to invent a plough which could be handled by one man on a tractor. Though a prodigious inventor of agricultural machinery, his main fault seems to have been a tendency to switch to his latest idea rather than perfect the machine on which he had till then been engaged.

Huxtables Plough Works

Anyone seeing the old plough works at West Buckland would find it hard to imagine the thriving engineering workshop described in the chapter on agricultural industries. The buildings have been converted into two semi-detached cottages, complete with flower gardens and climbing roses round the door. At the back of the buildings the room which once housed the waterwheel is now used as a larder. Only the wide chimneypieces in the living rooms remain to indicate that, at one time, several forges were kept going at full blast in order to keep up with the demand for Huxtables implements.

The works was abandoned in 1896 after a series of misfortunes, all connected with the waterwheel. The summer of 1895 had been marked by unusual long dry periods resulting in a shortage of water to drive the wheel; this was followed by a particularly hard winter which froze the leat and again left the works without power for several weeks. The final blow came in 1896 when a young boy, a relative of John Huxtable, was killed when trying to ride on the wheel. These events led to the factory moving to its present site in Alexandra Road, Barnstaple, into buildings which had previously housed Seldons clay tobacco-pipe factory. The machinery in the old Alexandra Road buildings was originally driven by a gas engine. This was removed some years ago, but one of the old lathes, reputed to have come from the West Buckland works, still remains, though no longer in use.

The present firm of Norrington & Huxtable has a large forge and several engineering workshops producing agricultural saw benches and several kinds of tractor-mounted implements, but they no longer make the ploughs and hay rakes which made the works famous throughout the Westcountry, and are now mainly concerned with the sale and maintenance of all kinds of agricultural machinery.

ARTICLE XI   CHAPPELE'S YARD TORRINGTON

Strong's argument for including Chappele's Skiver Dressing Yard at Torrington is a little difficult to follow, but there is no doubt that the tanning of leather was once an important industry in the area. Most north Devon towns had at least one tannery, but Torrington became quite a centre for the industry and at one time had five tanneries in addition to the Skivers yard. The buildings of three of them are still standing, and part of one has been converted for use as a cinema.

Most of the buildings which housed Chappele's Tannery have now been demolished though one has been kept in good repair and is used by a builders' merchants as a store.

The water-driven tucking mill at Weare Gifford, where all the fulling of the skins was carried out prior to the installation of steam engines at the Torrington yard, has had an interesting history of its own. Until 1850 when the tannery took it over, the mill housed Turton's Blanket Factory. Cloth for the blankets was probably woven in the villages and farms surrounding, but the mechanical processes of carding the wool, and fulling the cloth to shrink and felt it, were carried out at the mill.

The carding machine used in the mill survived until about 1950 in the workshop of a Torrington cabinet maker who used it for reflocking old mattresses. Unfortunately it was broken up when no longer needed, though it was photographed before being destroyed.

When the fulling mill was no longer needed by the tannery, all the machinery was dismantled and the building converted for use as a blacksmith's forge.

ARTICLE XII   FREMINGTON POTTERY

Fremington Pottery closed down between 1912 and 1914; the site is now occupied by Wrights, a small electrical engineering firm. Only the house and part of one of the store rooms of the old pottery still remain. The main products of the Fishley pottery—pitchers, pilchard stains, meat pickling pans, ovens, yeast and bread jars—were vessels used in the storing or preservation of foodstuffs and it is interesting to note that the electrical firm now on the site specialises in the manufacture of deep freeze refrigerators.

On the death of Edwin Beer Fishley in 1911, his grandson William Fishley-Holland carried on the firm for his two uncles. In 1912 he left and started his own pottery at Braunton. The Fremington Pottery was taken over by C. H. Brannam of Barnstaple but it was soon closed down and was demolished shortly afterwards.

In his book *Fifty Years a Potter* published by *Pottery Quarterly* in 1958, Mr Fishley-Holland has described his early life in Fremington Pottery. As a journeyman potter he was paid 21 shillings a week in 1912. Work started at 6am; breakfast was from 8 to 8.30. At 11am a cooked meal was provided and work started again at 11.30. There was a tea or coffee break at about 1pm then the afternoon's work continued until 6pm in summer or until it was too dark to see in winter. There was no lunch break on Saturdays but work finished at 4.30. On Fridays the firm ran a stall in Barnstaple Market.

The potters had to work hard as the retail price of their

goods was low even for those days. Ovens cost about 1½d per peck; if an oven's interior would hold eight pecks, its cost was 1s. Pitchers cost between 1½d for a 1½ pint size, to 7d for a 2 gallon one.

Fishley quay near the site of the old pottery is still visible but very outgrown and dilapidated. The quay was used by the small sailing coasters when loading cargoes of ovens and pottery for the ports of north Cornwall and Somerset.

ARTICLE XIII   MODEL FARMING AT
HIGHFORD, HARTLAND

Mr Berriman's design for a model farm has stood the test of time well and the description given by Strong remains a good guide to the property. Most of the changes have been internal rather than structural though the house has been extended and some modern buildings added. The stables, granary and cattle stalls are still as described in the chapter, except for the provision of modern milking and milling machinery. Water continues to be supplied by the reservoir near the Hartland Road. On completion of his improvements in 1907 Mr Berriman erected two gateways, one at each end of the property. These he named his Alpha and Omega gates. As the son of one of the present owners pointed out, 'Mr Berriman wanted to be remembered; his initials are on everything.'

ARTICLE XIV   MARLAND TERRA-COTTA
BRICK & STONEWARE PIPE WORKS

Clay beds in the Peters Marland basin have been worked for well over 300 years, the first records of operation dating from 1680. The clay continues to be worked by the North Devon

Clay Company, but the brick and tile works closed down in 1942. The buildings which, apart from the kilns, were mainly constructed of timber, were then used by the Ministry of Supply until August 1944 when fire broke out and destroyed most of the works. The kilns were later demolished and levelled to provide foundations for the present large sheds where the clay is processed, graded and stored. The company's workshops, offices and laboratory are also situated in this area, which is still known as Brickyards.

Unfortunately Strong has not given us a description of the clay workings in his account. This is not surprising, as a tour through the workings usually means wading through a sea of mud. Until the spring of 1969 the clay was extracted by both opencast and underground mining. The underground work was done in shallow timber-lined shafts which started with a short steep slope of about 50ft at an angle of about 45 degrees. This then levelled out to a slope of about one in five and continued underground for up to 700ft. Conditions in these workings were cramped and noisy, but surprisingly dry.

The hard clay was cut with heavy picks until compressed air shovels were introduced. Even with their aid, the work was extremely trying as the shovels, weighing about 50lb had to be held up to the roof of the shaft then brought downwards in an arc across the clay face and then lifted back to the roof for the next cut. A surface winding engine hauled the clay out of the shaft in a small truck, from which it was tipped into narrow gauge railway trucks waiting below the primitive wooden head gear.

The miners started work at 6am and worked through with short breaks until 1pm when they finished work for the day. This allowed the workings to be cleared of clay during daylight. The clay, which had to be kept dry, was then taken to the drying sheds to be stored before sorting and shredding.

Until the early 1930s the open pits were also worked with hand tools. The clay was first cut into rectangular blocks by downward strokes of a heavy wedge-like spade. These blocks or balls of clay were undercut and removed from the clay bed by an adze-like implement called a bale. The balls of clay, each weighing about 18lb were then thrown into a three sided truck which was hauled out of the pit up a ramp and emptied into one of the works railway trucks.

Clay is now dug from the two large pits by mechanical excavators and transported to the works railways in large tipping lorries. The 3ft gauge railway which serves the works and clay pits once ran all the way to the terminus of the London & South Western Railway at Torrington, a distance of about six miles. It was constructed in 1880 under the supervision of Mr Fell who also engineered the Mont Cenis railway in Switzerland. One of the features of this picturesque line was the large timber viaduct by which it crossed the river Torridge just before entering Torrington station. The line was closed in 1925 on the opening of the North Devon & Cornwall Junction Light Railway. Part of this line is still kept open for clay traffic as far as the English China Clay Company's workings at Meeth.

Fifty per cent of the clay from Peters Marland is exported. Clay destined for European ports is shipped from Fremington Quay near Barnstaple, while clay for North America is taken to Fowey. An increasing amount of the clay for the home market, is now dispatched by road. It is used mainly in the manufacture of high class earthenware, sanitary ware and tiles. At one time the company's advertisement recommended it as 'best tobacco-pipe clay'.

ARTICLE XV THE RALEIGH CABINET WORKS

The cabinet works is still in production, and during the past three years has been completely re-equipped with modern machinery. The exterior of the works has remained virtually unchanged over the years, though the old inscription 'Shapland & Petters High Class Cabinet Works' has now nearly vanished from one of the end walls.

Today the firm concentrates on the production of interiors for specialised buildings such as laboratories, schools and government offices. Another of their main lines is the production of ready made doors and door frames. At present they employ about 300 people, but the firm is planning to expand its workshop in the near future when the Ilfracombe branch line from Barnstaple is closed down. This line at present obstructs the factory entrance causing planning problems.

Some of the sturdily built machines described by Strong survived in working order right into the 1960s. The steam engines were used until 1927, but had been converted to drive generators instead of driving the machines via line shafting. One of the old Lancashire boilers now fired by wood shavings, is still used to provide steam and heating for various processes in the factory.

ARTICLE XVI Weare Gifford Flour Mill

Weare Gifford mill is easily seen from the road which joins the various parts of the village. The buildings are no longer used as a mill but from the outside it still looks much the same as it did at the time of Strong's visit. The interior of the mill has undergone several changes since 1889. The vector turbine was removed in about 1910 and replaced by one made in the USA. When the mill closed in 1940 this turbine was taken to Clapworthy Mill near South Molton where it still provides power for Hancocks Cider Factory.

Sometime after 1945 the mill was re-equipped with a waterwheel to drive machinery for a small patent hairgrip factory. This factory never went into production. One reason for this may have been that the wheel, which is still in place, seems to have been installed the wrong way round—in the overshot position when it should have been breast shot. The mill now houses battery chicken and pigs. None of the original machinery remains.

ARTICLE XVII   Exe Valley Fish
Breeding Establishment

In the past eighty years the Exe Valley Fish Farm has grown until it is now one of the largest in Great Britain. The original farm suffered a severe setback a few years after Strong's visit, when Mr Ashton the manager died. Mr Langdon, the owner of the establishment was not an expert at fish breeding and was forced to abandon the project some time in the mid-1890s.

During the early 1900s the buildings and ponds were sold to a Mr Tracy who had studied fish breeding at the Braunton fish farm owned by F. G. Richmond. Mr Tracy reconstructed and extended the premises and over the years established the hatchery's reputation for sound stock.

In 1927 the firm was sold to a Mr Young who operated it until 1954, when the present owner, Mr Maund, took over. He has carried out further extensions and improvements, so that the hatchery is now capable of breeding over 150,000 fish per year, the larger ones weighing up to 5lb.

The best view of the buildings and ponds is obtained from the old railway embankment on the western side of the river Exe. One of the features of the farm is a small watermill which has been used in the past to grind fish-meal. There has been a mill on the site since the Domesday survey but though the mill wheel is still intact some of the gearing has been removed and the mill is no longer in use.

The farm may have to close if the fish disease, Ulcerated Dermal Necrosis prevalent in many rivers, affects the breeding stock. A similar outbreak occurred in the early 1900s.

Industries

Of North Devon.

By *H. W. STRONG.*

REPRINTED FROM THE *NORTH DEVON JOURNAL.*

BARNSTAPLE :

W. Michael, Printer and Publisher, 95, High Street.

1889.

INDEX.

INTRODUCTORY.

THE series of articles which follows by no means exhausts the subject, and is not entirely representative. In and out of print, the request has been made, since their publication in the columns of the *North Devon Journal*, that the sketches, for the most part written at a single sitting, whilst the impressions of a two or three hours' visit to the manufactory or scene of industry were fresh in the memory, should be published in book form. The original purpose of their publication has been served, but it has been suggested that the descriptions will be of more than immediate interest, and that, as an original contribution to the history of the County of Devon, they will justify reproduction in a shape more likely to secure their permanence. It is necessary, however, that it should be understood that industries exist in North Devon which have no place in this series. This is not the fault of the writer, but the result of the scruples of the manufacturers themselves, which, however much he deplored their existence, he was bound to respect. Several of the industries described, too, exist in duplicate. An endeavour was made to select such manufactories as were representative of the staple trades of North Devon, and, if the important exception of tanning be made, there is no considerable labour-employing industry which is omitted.

The extent and variety of the industrial occupations of the population of North Devon appear not to have been generally known to the inhabitants themselves, much less to the outside world. As a matter of fact, however, the country between Hartland Point and Hangman Hill, Barnstaple and Southmolton, has for a long term of years boasted industries of an important character. Without attempting to enter into a question of such ancient history as is involved in the speculation of a geologist that Croyde Bay was the scene of a flint implement industry before the dawn of civilisation, and therefore the site of one of the

earliest manufactories of the country, it is by no means difficult to
establish a very "decent connection" between the locality of which Barnstaple is the metropolis and British manufactures. The seaboard gave
North Devon her trades, undoubtedly ; but, although to-day the tide of
commerce flows in other directions, and in the matter of railway
communication there is much to be desired locally, the isolation from
the great manufacturing centres of the kingdom has not destroyed
industrial enterprise. True, it has found other channels. The manufactories of the present day are not the natural descendants of those
which employed the labour of a hundred years ago. No longer can it
be said, in the words of Westcote, "Barnstaple and Torrington furnish
us bayes (baize), single and double, and fryzadoes, and such like ; and
Pilton, adjoining, vents cotton (a species of the coarsest woollen cloth) and
lyninge, so coarse a stuff as there was a væ (a woe) pronounced against
them in these words : ' Woe unto you, ye Piltonians, that make cloth
without wool.'" To-day Torrington (which was also a centre of the
woollen trade) and Pilton are engaged in different branches of the glove
trade, while Barnstaple has discarded wool in favour of cabinet and lace-
making. The connection between the Barum of centuries since and the
extending borough of to-day is, however, preserved by the potter's art,
which flourishes, with added celebrity, in its old haunts.

Barnstaple was formerly the chief Devonshire port for the importa-
tion of wool, but with the decay of her shipping there disappeared the
famous Barum "Bayes." The Rack Hayes, as one part of the North
Walk, where citizens now take the air, was formerly styled, is described
in records of the borough as an appendage, or relic, of the great industry
of the sixteenth and seventeenth centuries. The assumption is that a
portion of the Castle waste was occupied by racks, whereon the "bayes"
were hung to dry. In "Auld Lang Syne" the weaving of rushes was
carried on extensively in Seevers Lane, abutting on Queen Street,
"weavers" and "seevers" being understood as synonymous terms.
Then there were corn and fulling mills on the South Eaux (South Yeo),
that is, "the water of Portimore," now styled Cooney Gut. Previous
to the Civil War, there were twenty baize manufacturers in the place,
and Barnstaple was counted a manufacturing town of nothing short of

secondary importance in the county. Coarse serges for the American trade replaced the baize, to give way, in course of time, to the lace manufactory, first established at Raleigh. Curiously enough a third great industry had its rise at this place, which in turn had seen the manufactures of woollen cloth, lace net, and furniture.

Bideford's proudest historical association with trade is a first page in the history of the introduction of " the divine weed " into England. The discovery of Virginia by Sir Richard Grenville preceded the hey-day of the commercial glory of " the little white town on the hill." Then " Bideford, metropolis of tobacco, saw her Pool choked with Virginian traders and the pavement of her Bridgeland street groaning beneath the savoury bales of roll Trinidado, leaf and pudding." Later on Bideford shared with Barnstaple in the serge trade, a hundred and fifty serges a year being the average output in the early part of the present century. Collar factories have succeeded, and Barnstaple is now the imitator of the smaller sister borough, the collar, front, and shirt trade being on the eve of opening in the town on the Taw. From time immemorial potteries of common ware, in the manufacture of which Fremington clay has been employed, have existed at Barnstaple and Bideford.

At a period not so very remote there was an output of 900 bushels of culm a week at Tawstock, the mineral being also dug in the parishes of Heanton and Chittlehampton. The pit at Tawstock was abandoned in 1800. Coal is said to have been found in small quantities at Abbot-sham, and ochre and umbre at Eastdown and Berrynarbor. A member of the Pine-Coffin family set up a manufactory for grinding ochre in the former parish about 1745. An average of 45 tons per annum was shipped to London, but after three years' working Mr. Pine-Coffin abandoned the venture. Manganese mines at Westdown apparently proved no more remunerative, for they shared the same fate.

The lead mines of Combemartin have a more ancient and honourable history. They greatly enriched the treasuries of Edward I. and II. Their origin is hid in obscurity, but they were reopened in the reign of Queen Bess, when British commerce received so great an impetus. Discarded again their re working was recommended to the Long Parliament in 1659. 1813 saw another attempt to revive the enterprise, but four years sufficed for the cooling of the ardour of the latest company of merchant adventurers. A little industry of an entirely different character once flourished at Combemartin. Shoemaker's thread was extensively manufactured from hemp there grown. Rich iron stone was shipped from the neighbourhood to the works at Llanelly, 9293 tons being sent between 1796 and 1802.

Inland, Southmolton, North Tawton and Bishop's Morchard have been largely employed in manufacturing coarse woollens for the Continent, and before the Peninsular campaign the first-named town was a conspicuous seat of this trade.

Pipe-clay, at Wear Gifford, Petersmarland, and Petrockstowe, and brown clay, in the parish of Fremington, have been " raised " on an extensive scale ; and the four or five parallel courses, or stratified beds, of limestone which exist in North Devon have caused numerous lime works to spring into existence.

The herring fishery on the north coast of Devon, and the salmon season in the Taw and Torridge, are still relied upon by the waterside population of Clovelly and Appledore for a considerable contribution to their means of subsistence. A fleet of Brixham trawlers have found in the Bristol Channel a remunerative fishing ground, and Lundy Island has become the centre of another promising industry. Fish-curing was once a feature of the trade of Ilfracombe, and the Domesday Book mentions several salt works near the coast.

Sufficient has been said in this brief retrospect to show that the district has a not unworthy association with industrial occupations, and the hasty sketches of the principal employments of the present generation which occupy the succeeding pages may be left to tell their own story of the nature, variety and interest of the Industries of North Devon in 1889.

HUGH W. STRONG.

BARNSTAPLE, *July,* 1889.

Industries of North Devon.

I.—THE BARNSTAPLE FOUNDRY.

IN commencing a series of articles on the Industries of North Devon, it will not be deemed inappropriate if the subject of the inaugural notice is chosen, not so much on account of the extensive character of the works, or the amount of labour employed, as from the fact that in its rapid growth the industry typifies the progress which has, on the whole, been the chief characteristic of manufacturing enterprise in this division of the county within the last decade.

With the cabinet works of Messrs. Shapland & Petter rising, Phœnix-like, from their ashes, and taking unto themselves proportions which bid fair to dwarf the former manufactory at Rawleigh; the Derby lace works of the Messrs. Miller, the Pilton glove factory of Messrs. Baylis & Co., and the manufactory of Messrs. Brady, holding their own in the stress of competition, while lesser industries manifest unmistakeable signs of prosperity, this increase of manufacturing energy is fairly focussed at Barum. In the centres which radiate from the Metropolis of North Devon, also, the signs of activity are not wanting. The Appledore shipwrights are on "full time;" indeed, we have heard of "overtime" as being

B

the rule rather than the exception at the Appledore yards. Then, the collar and other factories at Bideford, if the ordinary signs of business are trustworthy, are in a flourishing condition. Though " slack " for the moment, the proprietors of Torrington glove works cannot complain of any decrease of output, and the locality can boast of an entirely new industry in the Torridge Vale Butter Factory.

But nowhere is this note of progress more emphatically sounded than at the Barnstaple foundry, which has extended its borders, taken unto itself wings, and, in fact, undergone a perfect revolution in its nature and extent.   If it is agreeable to the public mind, the completion of the conversion of the foundry into a modern industry, with all the newest appliances for the manufacture of iron work generally, may be character- ised as the celebration of the Jubilee of the concern.   It was just fifty years ago that Mr. Thomas Lamb Willshire laid the foundation of the business.   At his decease, it was taken over by his son, Mr. Charles Sweet Willshire, who carried it on until May of 1884, when Mr. W. C. Rafarel became the pro- prietor.   Within the year of the advent of their new master, the workmen of the foundry were apprised of the extensive alterations and additions to the works which he contemplated, with the view of introducing the appliances of modern inven- tion, enabling the local manufacturer to compete successfully with his rivals in the great centres of the iron industry.   The extension of the works has, we believe, even exceeded the original designs of Mr. Rafarel himself, and the foundry is now supplied with the latest advances of engineering skill on a scale which not only does credit to the enterprise of the merchant- proprietor, but reflects distinction upon the locality.   The foundry now has a frontage—extending from Victoria road to Newport terrace, and facing Nelson terrace—of some 150 yards. The works themselves, and the adjacent yards of the foundry, cover about an acre and a half of ground. The bulk of the works are contained in a square, the inside border of which is the stream issuing from Cooney Gut, which provides the water supply of the foundry. They occupy about fifty yards at the widest part, narrowing down to thirty or forty feet at the Victoria road end. Over fifty hands are employed in the various departments.

The old foundry, in its extent, and its labour-employing capacity, was about a third of the size of the present prosperous industry. The site of the original works has been utilised for the show-rooms and warehouses of the business. A dead wall, flanking the old foundry, has given place to glass fronts, with ornamental pillars and railings. Here are the show windows, in which the more attractive manufactures are set out. Even the old boiler stack has been transformed into something more of "a thing of beauty," with a light ornamental railing surmounting it. On gaining the interior, it is discovered that the foundry has been converted into a warehouse. The old buildings, which have, however, been entirely re-roofed, have readily lent themselves to the metamorphosis. The main ware-room is a lofty building, with corrugated galvanized iron roofing, and skylights. Here an immense stock of rain and hot water goods, horse nails, furnaces, pigs' troughs, &c., is stored. The lower portion is occupied with hardware. Vertical and saddle boilers, circulating cylinders, and iron supply tanks are pushed to the front. But, harking back to the rain water goods, for the show of which it is claimed that it exceeds in quantity and

B 2

variety most stocks in the West of England, we are reminded
that merchants excel in the merits of their wares as *litterateurs*
do in the products of their authorship, and to the works of the
manufacturer some such compliment may be paid as that earned
by " rare Ben Jonson : "

> " The Alchemist," " The Fox," and " Silent Woman,"
> Done by Ben Jonson, and outdone by no man.

Plough metal is stored to the right of the principal wareroom,
and the old fitting shop now serves as the stable fittings, steam
pipes, and oils and colours' department.   The old smithy now
serves the purpose of an extensive store for register and tile
grates, and Cobbett stoves.   This department is, together with
that of galvanized goods, one of the staple features of the
" wholesale merchant " side of the house.   It abuts upon the
lofty ironmonger's shop, which is an entirely new department
of the concern.   A good frontage and an airy interior give an
attractive appearance to the fresh premises.   The stock chiefly
consists of builders' ironmongery, steam fittings, belting,
hose, &c.   There is an iron store over the old entrance, and the
original offices have been utilised for metal stores.   This completes the extent of the premises purchased by Mr. Rafarel,
and the larger half of the foundry which remains to be
described is the accretion of the past four years, during which
the enterprise of the proprietor has manifested itself in a very
marked manner.

A suite of offices occupy the extended frontage.   The cash-
ier's department admits to the employer's office, that of the
managing foreman (Mr. Jarvis) succeeds, the timekeeper's
room completing the suite.   The managerial departments are
thus consolidated under one roof —an arrangement which has

its obvious advantages.   The offices occupy the site of the old
ironmongery department.   At the cleaning shop we commence
the round of the foundry proper, and thus early attention
is drawn to the fact that man has sought out many inventions
in this sphere of British manufacturing enterprise.   The circular brush worked by machinery has replaced the old system of
hand cleaning.

Arrived at the rear of the warehouses, the water supply of
the foundry is investigated.   The supply is drawn from Cooney
Gut by means at once ingenious and economical.   A filter bed
has been constructed at the level of the stream.   The water
passes through the bed into a well, from whence a donkey
pump forces it into a receiver, which acts as a reservoir, and is
at a sufficient height to supply the whole of the foundry.   The
new boiler house is an impressive feature of the works.   The
boiler is of 20 horse-power, nominal.   Vertical boilers are
taken about by the workmen of the firm in carrying out the
various contracts and jobs executed in different parts of the
country, four engines and boilers being on hand for this
purpose.   The large stationary boiler is served with its water
supply by a donkey engine.   The stack of the boiler towers
above the building some sixty odd feet.   In the engine room,
the principal engine drives the machinery of the fitting shop
immediately adjoining, and blows the blast for the smithy
across the yard ; for steam and blast purposes the two lines of
workshops are connected.   Root's Patent Blower, for the cupola,
and Schiele's Patent Fan, for the smithy, are two remarkable
productions of modern engineering included among the manufacturing facilities of the foundry.   Driven by the engine
already noticed, large and small planing machines, a large

boring machine—capable of boring wheels up to 18 feet—
a lathe for heavy shafting, a large screw-cutting machine, and
a self-acting screw-cutter, are seen at work in the fitters' department, together with other and smaller screw-cutting lathes,
two double-geared, and one single-geared, drilling machine.
Here, in course of manufacture, are chaff-cutters and pulpers,
malt mills for export, horse-gearing, self-acting screw-cutting
and surfacing lathes, engine fittings, pistons and rings, among
a host of etceteras.　The motor power generated in the engine
room is further utilised in working a coal grinding machine,
which manufactures a mixture for facing in the moulding
department.　　In the open space between the fitting shop
and smithy, 400 tons of pig and scrap iron are stored, and the
customary conveniences of work employing a number of hands
have been erected.　　Across the yard comes the mighty music
of the anvils, reviving in the memory the clanging chorus
of "The Four Jolly Smiths : "

> With a bang, and a clang, and a ding, ding, dong,
> The work goes merrily rolling along.

The weighbridge will occupy a corner of the yard, from
whence steps lead to the pattern makers' shop and lofts, which
range over the offices and the fitters' department.　An extraordinary collection of almost every conceivable pattern of
fittings is this, and it is said to have but one co-extensive rival
in the Western counties. Birmingham is credited with manufacturing everything from a pin to a steam engine, and here
we seem to see preparation made for casting anything from a
mill-wheel to the smallest cog of the minutest machine. Pillars
for churches, pillars for gate entrances, panel cresting for bal-
conies, verandahs, and conservatories, hay machine fittings,

reaper, corn and turnip drill, and winnowing machinery, mill-gearing and ships' pumps—it would exhaust the catalogue of a machine manufacturer to name the patterns that are confusing in their multitude and manifold shape and design.

But we hie to the habitation of the sons of Vulcan, the divine blacksmith, whose workshop was on Mount Etna, where the Cyclops assisted him in forging thunderbolts for Jove. Mr. Rafarel's men are less classically, but quite as usefully, employed. There are six fires in the smithy, with nine black-smiths at work at and about the iron forges. The blast for the six fires, as has been already mentioned, is supplied from the Schiele's Fan across the way, and so perfect is the system that as the visitor, stirred by old associations, tries to

> Catch the burning sparks that fly
> Like chaff from a threshing floor,

the fierceness of the fire is regulated from white heat to a dull glow by an arrangement that admits of the gentlest gradation. Tubes convey the smoke from the six forges to the large stack in the centre, and the constant current of air through the chimney so adulterates the smoke that the chances of a nuisance being created are reduced to a minimum. As a mat-ter of fact, the dwellers in the neighbourhood of the foundry have no cause of complaint on this score, and that they do not complain is sufficient proof that this is the case. General forgings of an ordinary character—railings being a principal " line "—are the productions of this department ; grates and their fittings are also manufactured here.

The Smithy, like the other buildings, is constructed of

corrugated galvanised iron, coated with oxide paint.   Hubert
tells the monarch in *King John :—*

> I saw a smith stand with his hammer thus,
> The whilst his own iron did on the anvil cool,
> With open mouth swallowing a tailor's news ;

but these are fairly busy times at Barnstaple foundry, and the
anvils ring to the measured rhyme of the smiths' hammers
incessantly.

" Here's metal more attractive," however. In the plumbers'
and coppersmiths' shop, at the inner end of the Smithy, are
brass and copper air furnaces.   Street lanterns are being made
for a Local Board ; hot water work is in hand ; and the lead,
zinc, and tin departments are well furnished with material.

The new foundry completes the square of fresh erections.
It is a long and lofty oblong building, in which a dozen or
fifteen men and boys are employed.   Castings, to the weight
of five tons, can be executed here.   Iron pillars support a line
of rails on which a travelling crane, capable of lifting five tons,
runs.   The pilasters of the loop line iron bridge over the Taw
were cast here, each individual mould weighing twenty-six
hundred weight.   A large amount of work is turned out here
for local builders.   Street lamp pillars, water wheels, gas and
water work castings, malt mills and engine work are some of
the principal "lines " of the foundry.   A large order for patent
axle boxes, from one of the great export firms, is being executed.   The doubling of the railway line to Ilfracome has also
brought " grist to the mill."

The core-drying stove, at the further corner of the foundry,
is a further illustration of the economic principle on which the
machinery of the establishment is worked ; the stove is heated

from the boiler across the yard, from whence pipes convey the steam. The core-house is next the stove. But we have over-looked a novel and a striking feature of the foundry. This is the " cupola " that fronts it—an improved metal furnace, con-nected with Root's Patent Blower over the way. In this furnace is applied the new principle of carrying the blast in two belts around the cupola, by which the maximum result is obtained at the minimum cost.

In the large yard for boxes those of the pilasters for the iron bridge over the Taw are noticed. The pilasters were manufac-tured and fixed by employés of Mr. Rafarel, who also rivetted the bridge, the contract being carried out to the entire satisfac-tion of the Company and the Government Surveyor. Stables and shedding complete the order of the buildings, and the survey of the works.

The rapidity with which the foundry has grown is, in no small degree, the outcome of the indication that the works have, in many respects, proved advantageous to the other in-dustries of the neighbourhood. The Barnstaple foundry now has a range of business extending over Devon, Cornwall and Somerset, whilst the London and export trades are constantly making a demand upon its greatly improved resources. This is not only satisfactory as a reward for private enterprise, but is especially gratifying from a public point of view, inasmuch as it enhances the commercial prosperity of Barnstaple, and, consequently, of North Devon.

II.—THE DERBY LACE FACTORY.

An industry which has existed for sixty-three years, which has caused a little town to spring up around it, receiving its appellation, and which has revolutionised the mechanism of its textile manufacture—must needs have an early notice in any account of the larger business concerns of North Devon. The Derby lace factory of Messrs Miller Brothers makes an important contribution to the commercial prosperity of the locality by the employment of some two hundred and fifty men, women and children of the wage-earning classes—indoor and outdoor hands, and that section of the industrial population beloved of the educationists, "half-timers." The Derby factory is a many-sided industry. It is an independent institution. The manufacture of the exceedingly ingenious machinery by which the lace is made goes on in another wing of the extensive premises, simultaneously with the lace making itself. The manufacturing colony at Derby, emulating the spirit of Juan Fernandez, holds undisputed sway over a little world of its own. Isolated from the centre of the lace making trade, for obvious reasons it keeps itself very much to itself. So far as the mechanical side of the factory is concerned its economical system is perfect. Demand and supply, exhaustion and reproduction goes on within the works, as if the proprietors of the industry had taken as the motto of their manufactory the dignified position which Mrs. Mona Caird demands as the rights of the two parties to the marriage contract, informing the curious interested crowd that it is not their business, and that their room is preferred to their company, curiosity or assistance.

The variety and the intricacy of the work carried on at the Derby lace factory handicaps the descriptive writer, upon whom it devolves to translate the technical language of the lace-maker into an idiom understood of the people. We are apprised of this difficulty immediately our courteous guide takes us under his wing at the counting house door; and the clatter of the multitudinous machinery, the sight of the rows of dexterous workers, deftly controlling this machinery with eye and hand so alert and active as to remind us of the old lady who protested that it required "eyes in the back of your head and two pair of hands" to discharge her culinary duties, and at the same time control the Columbus-like voyages of her numerous progeny—these, together, apprise us of the difficulties of the task we have undertaken in attempting to convey to the public what we have seen with our eyes and endeavoured to understand, in its elementary principles.

But we have a preliminary word or two to say about the history of the factory, which is not uninteresting. In the fourteenth century, woollen manufactories were flourishing in Barnstaple—a fact deposed to by the Borough Records, in which is cited a petition to Edward II., in 1308 "to have the custom imposed 28 Edward I., taken off." Pilton was one of the original seats of this industry, and "Rawleigh flannels" were manufactured down to 1795, when a fire, supposed to have been the work of an incendiary, consumed the cotton mill, with its machinery, and the concern was abandoned. In 1821, the uninjured building remaining at Rawleigh was purchased by lace factors, from Nottingham and Derby, and converted into a manufactory for bobbin net. This was the origin of the business now carried on at the Derby lace factory, which, so far as the material manufactured is concerned, is of precisely the same nature as at the commencement of the industry, although strange vicissitudes and mutations have marked the history of the local factories. In about four years from the reopening of the Rawleigh works, a dissolution of partnership

among the original proprietors led to the establishment of the
new concern in Vicarage-lane now under notice. Mr. Bowden
was the enterprising factor who laid the foundation of an industry which has from 1825 to the present day been one of the
staple supports of the trade of Barnstaple.   For the first time
in the history of lace-making, locally, the whole of the machinery
of the new manufactory was propelled by steam, for which
purpose an engine of sixteen horse power was employed.   Here
we have, in one concrete fact, the whole history of the de-
velopement of this industry illustrated to us.   The engine
which now drives the vastly improved and immensely increased
machinery, is of 60 horse power, nominal.   When we remember
that the engineering skill of the past half century has doubled,
if not trebled, the productive power and the executive action
of steam, we have some idea of the growth of the Derby
factory.   It is now carried on upon a scale at least five times
larger than when the corner stone of populous Derby was laid
by Mr. Bowden.   That gentleman hailed from the great
manufacturing town of Derby, then one of the seats of the
machine made lace trade.   Hence the name by which we know
the neighbourhood of thickly-clustered dwelling houses that
environ the factory.

It may assist us in arriving at a conclusion as to why the
site of the factory was chosen for the offstart from the Rawleigh
business if we remember that Vicarage or Stony-bridge lane,
which runs around Frankmarsh and Rawleigh, was the original,
and, in the days of our great-great-grandsires, the only access
to Pilton, when the fosse or causeway existed, which preceded
the bridge ; the river Yeo was then impassable, as a good woman
of Pilton found to her loss, for she was carried away by the tide
when attempting to ford the river.

In the year that saw Derby factory established, another branch of the Rawleigh concern was set on foot by " an enterprising and ingenious person who was employed at Rawleigh, and had a principal share in the superintendence of the machinery there." He erected a mill adjoining the London road, and about a quarter of a mile from the town, commencing with a modest display of machinery, the whole concern being worked by a steam engine of 8 h.p. Within five years there had thus been set on foot three large manufactories. Together, they employed one thousand persons. In connection with the last named factory, there was a sale and show-room in Barnstaple, where worked-lace dresses, veils, &c., were " finished " and retailed. It is not inappropriate that this article should follow the notice of the Barnstaple foundry which appeared last week, for, as a matter of fact, the establishment of the lace industry in the neighbourhood was one of the principal causes of the starting of the foundry itself.

The Rawleigh manufactory, as we are well aware, was, in the course of time, transformed into cabinet works, and the mill on the London road had no great success. The Derby factory was destined to hand on, maintain, and extend the association of Barnstaple with the lace-making industry. Mr. John Miller, father of the present proprietors, purchased the mill from the original owner, Mr. Bowden. The growth and improvement of the concern may be dated from the time of this transaction. At the decease of Mr. Miller, the business was carried on by his Trustees in the interest of his children until the three brothers who constitute the present firm attained their majority. Messrs J. M. Miller and A. H. Miller conduct the bobbin-net manufactory at Barnstaple ; the third brother,

Mr. W. W. Miller, managing the wholesale house at Nottingham, where the ware and sale rooms are, and the goods are disposed of.

The advent of Messrs. Miller at the Vicarage-lane manufactory was the signal for new departures in the machinery of the works. The intelligent mechanics employed in the various departments brought their practical knowledge to bear upon labour saving and time-economising contrivances, and, stimulated by the approval, encouraged by the enterprise, and assisted by the skill of their employers, in course of time they vastly improved the mechanism of the whole mill machinery. " Mum is the word " concerning these trade secrets, though many a rival manufacturer would give his ears to possess them. In the course of our notice, however, it will transpire where improvements have been introduced, though so busy have been the active minds and keen eyes of the leading workmen of the establishment that it would be difficult to say where the old order ended giving place to the new.

The Works (compact as they are), together with the accommodation land attached to the factory, cover over an acre of ground. The factory itself occupies three sides of a square. Looking in at the principal entrance, where many a lace machinist, excusably jealous of the secrets of the trade carried on within, has stood, like Moore's Peri at the gate of Paradise, disconsolate, the mill faces us. Immediately on our left is the commodious counting house of the firm. In the further corner are the fitters' and smiths' shops. The lofty building on our right is a continuation of the mill, where the new rolling locker machines were introduced some twelve years since, and where mechanical improvements continue to be the order of the day.

Ere we survey the interior of the factory, a word should be said of the introduction of machinery into lace making by twisted threads. We have no such romantic story to tell of the bobbin net as is related of Venetian point lace, with its beautiful design and perfect make, which lace traditions associate with its suggestion to a girl whose lover brought to her from the Southern sea a present of coral. But the individual who is responsible for the saying that, as truth may be found in the bottom of a well, so there is always a woman at the bottom of every disturbance of preconceived ideas, has another tribute to his insight in the history of the machine-made bobbin net. A machine known by the euphoneous name of the spoon tickler, covering two needles and delivering the stitch on both, had been introduced by a frame-smith of Nottingham. One day in 1768, a drunken, but clever workman, named Hammond, sat in a public house at Nottingham, as he had often sat before, drinking with his wife. Hammond was thoroughly conversant with the meshing art. The " happy pair " are described as being without money, credit, or regular employment, and intoxicated into the bargain, when Hammond cast his lack-lustre eye upon the broad lace border on his wife's cap, and a lace caul, and thought he could imitate the fabric. Hammond became the inventor of the Nottingham bobbin net; " working by day and drinking by night ; thus passed several years of the life of this original machine wrought--lace manufacturer." While blear-eyed Hammond sat in the pot house, a boy named John Heathcoat, living with his mother at Long Whatton, in Leicestershire, heard a "slip of a girl " who used to come to see his mother, tell of her cousin who had been employed at the factory of one Dawson in London, whom she described as

having made a fortune by machinery.   The pert lass turned
round to John, and said, jocularly, " Why can't you do so too,
John?" Forty years after, in 1808, John Heathcoat—the boy
of 1768, though scarcely recognisable—of Nottingham, obtained
patents for machines for making bobbin, which formed the real
foundation of the machine making of lace.

This brief excursion into lace history will assist us in
appreciating the advances in mechanical ingenuity which have
been applied to the manufacture at the Derby factory.   Now
we will follow the thread from its receipt at the mills, to its
departure, in the metamorphosed and intricate form of
bobbin-net.   The thread is supplied to Messrs. Miller Bros.
from the Lancashire cotton mills, the Manchester and Oldham
cotton spinners having the major part of the orders of the firm.
It arrives in bulk, by rail, and is deposited in the receiving
house, at the left hand corner of the large central mills.   Each
bundle of thread is here weighed.   Skeins from the bulk are
then placed upon testing machines, which are the first of many
ingenious specimens of the machinist's art with which we are
destined to be familiarised in the factory.   This tests the
" hanks " for " count " (size) and strength.   In the receiving
room we are also acquainted with the fact that, although
neither of the members of the firm is a barrister, they all, in
unison, " receive silk."   The cocoons of the silkworms of China
Bengal, and Italy, have supplied the throwster with these
brightly-coloured skeins that dazzle the eye unused to such a
wealth of warm hues.   Thread and silk are given out here for
the operation called " preparing " which lucidly explains its
purpose   Each bundle is weighed and ticketed with the
receiver's factory number—you sink your individuality in the

mill, and become a unit of its active whole. This enables it
to be traced and any defect to be discovered and ascribed to
the proper quarter. After the " preparing " process is completed, the " hanks " are weighed and tested, before they are
passed on to the winding room. Following the skeins to this
department, we are made acquainted with some of the most
modern machinery introduced into the trade by Messrs. Miller
themselves. The desideratum of the machinery is its advantage over the old system in compactness : the maximum of
work is accomplished at the minimum expenditure of labour.
Here the silk is wound from skeins or hanks, the machine girls
being as nimble with their fingers as they are alert with their
eyes. The agricultural visitor, dropping all promiscuously into
the preparing room of the factory, might be bewildered by the
similarity of the " swifts " to his own haymakers, but he will
soon be apprised of the wide distinction that exists, in the
beauty and dexterity of the machinery employed. From the
winding rooms, the bobbins are taken back to the preparing
room, where they are weighed and tested, and the results
compared with the ticket issued with the bundle in the first
place. With some of the coarser cottons, there is an intermediate
process between the receiving and the issuing to the preparers.
This is the damping of the cotton, which assists in the manufacture of the lace by rendering the thread more susceptible to
the flattening process which facilitates the work of the lace-
maker. This process is carried on in the damping department
at the rear of the mill, where a centrifugal drying machine,
worked by steam, enamel lined and lead-lined cisterns, are in
use. Hanks of thread of the coarser " numbers " are laid on
the floor and slightly damped, after which they are passed on
to the preparing machine.

C

In separate rooms, Bengal and Italian silk is being unwound from hanks and wound on to bobbins. The Italian silk requires special treatment and distinct machinery. In this instance, the silk is drawn on to blocks, and then wound on to the bobbins, travelling " guides " spreading the silk as it passes on to the bobbins.

From the second weighing a part of the thread is conveyed to the warping room to be made into warps. We will follow it there that we may further unravel the mystery of the manufacture of the net-mesh for which all this elaborate preparation is made. A number of the wood bobbins are placed upon spindles in a frame, technically called a " scullum " and the ends of the thread are drawn on to the beam of the warping mill in a double layer, through brass plates of the " guage " of the lace-machine the warp is prepared for. Having received instructions as to the length of the warp, the warper so sets the machine that at the completion of the winding of every hundred yards a bell connected with the warping mill shall be rung, and, when each " lay " of the warp is the required length it shall automatically throw itself out of gear. A number of " lays," all of the same length, are then successively placed on the machine until the width required for the lace machine is attained. In the orderly, consecutive steps in the progress of bobbin-net manufacture, the " lays " are now turned off from the " beams " on to the rollers that are used in the lace machines. Akin to the mythological figure that stoops over the " warp " and " woof " of life to check its irregularities and facilitate the interlacing of the lines of human destiny, here the " hand " takes great care during this process to remedy any defects from broken threads, and to make the warp as perfect as possible. From the warping mill, the rollers are taken, weighed, and ticketed. They are now ready to be given to the lace hands.

There are a few other features of the warping mills to which we must pay attention, but unless the processes of manufacturing the lace are described in consecutive order, the difficulty of making the system clear will be increased. We have seen how the warp thread is prepared for the machine and the woof must now engage our attention. What we will, for the sake of convenience, call the woof thread (the lace hands style it the bobbin thread) is carried on in a brass wheel bobbin, which plays the part of the old weaver's shuttle. It is small wheel with its outer edge open to receive the thread to a certain depth, near its boss. The thread is wound on this bobbin by special machinery, the winding being accomplished with a tension regulated by an ingenious contrivance. Space will not permit us to dwell upon this splendid specimen of automatic machinery. It stops when the thread breaks, and when the line of bobbins are full; in fact, as Lord C. Beresford has said, "it does everything but talk." Human skill comes into evidence again at the sight of the carriages which contain the brass bobbins in the lacemaking machine, and here we have a wonderful exhibition of what trained hands can accomplish. When the bobbins are full, they are packed into specially made boxes, and, by means of lifts, distributed to the machines for which they are intended. The lads who now take the end of the bobbin thread, and simultaneously carry it through the eye of the carriage in which it works, catch the spring, and place the bobbin within its circle, as the delicate spring comes back to snap and hold it in its place, are extraordinary adepts at

c 2

their work, and it wants the accustomed eye to detect each individual movement. After every piece of net comes out of the machine, something like 3,960 carriages (now more, now less) have thus to be filled in time for the manufacture of the new piece; and three such pieces are completed at each machine in two days. The boy whom we watch has thread up and the lace hand has set 2,496 carriages for the machine of which he has the control.

But we must retrace our steps for a moment, to explain that, for the manufacture of silk nets, the preparation differs a little from that described in the case of cotton. And here, whilst speaking of nets, and more especially of the silken of that ilk, let it be understood that Jonathan Swift's keen shaft of satire : " the reason why so few marriages are happy is because young ladies spend their time in making nets, not in making cages," was never intended to particularly apply to any section of the fair sex. In the first place the skeins of silk are " drammed " —that is, carefully weighed and sorted to size. Then it is given out to be wound on wood bobbins. Its next destination is a " drumming frame," where about 180 threads are drawn down over a black board, which intuitively plays the part that the motto of the North Devon Athenæum commends : " What is in me dark illumine." It clearly reveals all the imperfections, which are carefully removed by skilled workers. As the ends pass on to the drum on which they are wound, they set in motion a clock which records the number of yards. From the " drums," when full, the warps are " beamed " and made, and the little brass bobbins are filled. Then " exit " silk to fill the capacious maw of the lace machines.

By the preparing room, the warping mill, the drumming

Plate 1 (above) The main nineteenth-century building of the Derby Lace Factory, Barnstaple; *2 (below)* steam powered bobbin-net machine of about 1840. Machines similar to this are still working at the Derby Lace Factory

Plate 3 (above) Pilton
Fellmongers Yard, 1864. The
glove factory, the tall
building on the left-hand side
of the lane, was supplied with
leather and chamois from
this yard; 4 (left) Brannam'
Barnstaple Pottery, Litchdor
Street

room, and the wheel winding department, we have at length
reached the lace making machinery proper. Machine bobbin-
net, when quite plain, is made by the to-and-fro movement of
the "carriage" and their bobbin threads, together with the
motions of the various sets of threads, warp, or bobbin. The
complexity of the machines which bewilder the visitor to gaze
upon and deafen him with their clatter—the lace maker tells
us, and we are perfectly credulous creatures—is due to the
mechanism by which the lateral movements are produced.
There is an almost maddening variety of movement, and it is
only by the closest attention, and the most assiduous instruc-
tion on the part of the intelligent guide, that visitors are
enabled to grasp the sequence of the movements. The machine
itself seems endowed with intelligence, and as for the workman, *he* appears to be little more than a vigilant spectator for
the moment, until we observe that he is on the alert, and his
eyes run to and fro, noticing the threads, bobbins, carriages,
points, and guides passing with, to us, exasperating rapidity
before him.

The three Fates, according to the Roman mythology, spin the
thread of life, the pattern being the events which are about to
occur. "Warp" and "woof" are oft in the poet's eye, as the
semblance of life's chequered maze, which is much like the
mesh, interlaced as it is with sunshine and sorrow. Grey
irefully sang, in "The Bard:"

> Weave the warp, and weave the woof,
>   The winding sheet of Edward's race,
> Give ample room, and verge enough,
>   The characters of hell to trace.

The lace machine, as it presents itself to the mechanic,

consists of a large iron frame, varying in length from 90 to
220 inches, according to the width of the net it is required to
make from it.   Attached to it are a great number of bearings
cams, wheels, springs, and levers, which give the motions
requisite to the formation of the net.   Running along the
whole length of the frame of the machine are two parallel bars,
one on each side, to which are fastened accurately-shaped strips
of brass, technically called either " circles " or " combs, " according to the form in which they are made.   These are fitted
so as to leave, in different frames, spaces varying from five
up to twelve to the inch.   These spaces define the " guage " of
the machine by their various widths. Above the "circles" appear
two rows of needle-like points, fitting the one into the hollow
of the other.   The distance the points are apart corresponds
to the spaces under them.   Over this again is a large roller
which winds up the work as it is made.   Along the centre of the
machine, and between the two rows of " circles," room is left
to allow the warp threads to pass from underneath.   Immediately under this open space are two bars provided with
" guides," and under this again the roller containing the warp.
The threads composing the warp are each threaded through one
of the eyes in the guides, then brought up through the machine
and fastened to the winding-up roller already mentioned.

The bobbins and carriages, all properly " threaded up " and
" set " as we have seen them, are next placed in two rows, into
the " circles."   All the ends of the threads are fastened to the
same roller as the warp threads, and the machine is then set in
motion.   Now, watch the movements which actually constitute
lace making by machinery.   The bobbins and carriages move
from one side to the other with a pendulum-like motion, passing

between the warp threads, as well as travelling through the
entire length of the machine, changing places as they arrive at
the ends, until the row, which was in front at starting becomes
the back row, and *vice versa.* This they continue to do, until
the piece of net has been made the required length. At the
same time that the bobbins are travelling, the warp threads
are also in motion, allowing the carriages to pass, now on one
side of them, then the other. When, in this way, the required
amount of "twist" has been put on, a row of the points previously noticed goes down among the threads, gathers up the
"twist" and holds it in position, until the second row of points
has performed a like movement, bringing up the other half of
the mesh, which is thus completed. During the whole of the
time the piece of net is making, the winding up roller at the
top of the machine is in constant motion, its "pull" being
automatically regulated by a most ingenious contrivance which
secures that, however much the size of it may be increased by
the net already made on it, the roller winds from the warp but
just sufficient at a time to keep the length of the mesh all
through precisely the same as when the machine was first
started on the manufacture of the piece.

The difficulty of describing a lace machine, and something
of the intricacy of its marvellous mechanism, may be conveyed
to the mind of the reader when it is stated that in the latest
production of the Messrs. Miller, 14,550 distinct pieces, independent of the bobbins and carriages, went to the building
up of the machine, each individual piece having to be handled
singly. The weight of this machinery was seven-and-a-half
tons. In addition to this, there are 3,960 brass bobbins and
iron carriages, these weighing by themselves three-and-a-half

cwt. And be it remembered that the failure of the smallest piece of machinery will not only throw the whole thing out of gear, but involve the destruction of the machine itself. For the ordinary make of net sixteen distinct motions are required to form each mesh, whilst some qualities necessitate twenty-four.

From the cylinder of the machine the lace net, which is the sole manufacture at Derby, is taken to the wareroom ; there it is weighed and registered, then handed out, to be finally dealt with in the mending and finishing rooms. The silk menders work on the premises in airy, well-lighted rooms, illuminated at night with the Wenham gaslight. They sit in groups with the lace in loops before them, or wound on rollers and stretched on frames. The work is received from the mill, ticketed, and given out to menders. Outdoor menders are employed in mending the cotton nets. They return them to the wareroom, where, by the "clearers," the ends and tags are removed, and the whole net "picked over." When thoroughly completed, to the satisfaction of the overlooker, the nets are taken to the folding room. The folding is systematically done, during the day by female hands, and at night by the watchman. The long nets are stretched on the folding frame, looped and placed in layers across and upon each other, until the whole piece is stretched on the frame, from whence it is taken to be again doubled, until it developes into a bulky package with the ticket upwards, and is deposited in the packing-room. Now it is placed in bags, and is then ready for the railway van. By special arrangement with the railway authorities, the lace goods despatched in the afternoon at three o'clock are delivered at the wholesale house of the firm in Nottingham at seven o'clock next morning, The packages travel by the London and South Western Railway to Waterloo, from whence they are conveyed across London to the Euston Street Station of the London and North Western Railway, which takes them on to Nottingham.

The passage of the material, from the thread to the textile fabric—from the skein to the lace—from Lancashire to Derby factory, and thence to the Nottingham house of Messrs. Miller —having been consecutively described, it remains for us to gather up the loose threads of our account of the manufactory. What we are doing with the scattered ends of our notes the " half-timers " and " raw hands " at Derby are daily performing with the cotton and silk threads which may have been snapped in winding on to the brass bobbins. In one of the lower rooms a score of girls are engaged unwinding broken thread from the brass bobbins, tieing the pieces and winding them on to wooden bobbins. Here the newcomers learn that dexterity and nimbleness which is rewarded with " promotion " to a position among the regular hands of the establishment.

In the " Drumming " room fine silk, as filmy as gossamer, is seen, and a mechanical " pet " of the firm is an ingenious machine for the winding on to the brass bobbin of this delicate thread. This is only another example of that mechanical genius whose handiwork displays itself throughout the factory. We met it down in the machine room half-an-hour since, when, in sharp comparison, we saw the lace making machine of say a decade since, and the improved article of almost human intelligence that stood beside it in the same wonderland of mechanical contrivance. Amidst the bewildering maze of movement, and the din and racket of the wilderness of wheels and bars, and cylinders and bobbins, this one striking **fact** of rapid progress and continuous enterprise impressed itself upon the mind.　Ninety lace making machines, beside all the warping mills and winding machines mentioned, are included in the works, the rolling-locker machine being the latest development of the devising brain and the skill of the fitter.

But in delicate touch and poise the human hand is still superior to the machine, however animated with intellect the latter may seem.　In the "Drumming" room the overlooker is "dramming" (weighing and sorting) the silk skeins, and the quickness of her hands deceives our eyes easily.

In silk, Chantilly and Cambray laces are manufactured. Mosquito, Brussels and Mechlin lace is made in cotton.　The net is sold "in the brown,"—that is to say, no finishing is done by Messrs. Miller Brothers.　A not inconsiderable portion of their lace, after it has been purchased of them, is now embroidered in Switzerland.　The nets are sold by the "rack "— that is according to the number of meshes.　A "rack" consists of 210 meshes.

A last word must be given to the "black arts" by which all the machinery which has been revolving around and about us as we have taken our survey of the factory is worked.　The motive power is centred in the boiler house, abutting on the well-tilled allotments, some three-quarters of an acre in extent, which the firm have let out to their workmen.　Here are two boilers, each of 50 horse-power, nominal.　They drive a com pound, high and low pressure condensing engine, of 60 horsepower, ordinarily working at 50.　The improving hand of the inventor is seen again in this department.　Regular speed has been obtained, in spite of the deviations of the engine, and the desideratum of sustained and undeviating action, which is such a necessity in the business, secured by another clever contrivance. All the steam supplied to the factory is lubricated. There is a condensing engine attached, and a donkey engine for the water supply. The coal sheds lie at the back of the boiler house, and in the yard between this and the blacksmith's shop is another thread store. The blacksmith's shop, with its three fires, carries its smoke to one flue, and avoids creating a smoke nuisance.

Entering the fitting shop, we discover the secret of the factory's greatness. There, in close confabulation, masters, foremen, and workmen oft do congregate to hammer out upon the anvil of their thoughts some " new invented plan " for improving the machinery of the mills, and their combined ideas are forged into the malleable iron which is to their inventive genius as clay in the hands of the potter. Suffice it to say that here are manufactured those splendid monuments of mechanical engineering skill which we have seen in the mill. Here is a slotting machine, for morticing iron, cutting key-ways in wheels, &c. ; there the cunning artificers are engaged at a self-acting lathe. Wheel-cutting machines, screw-cutting lathes, &c., lace making machines, warp mills, and the thousand and one etceteras of the minutiæ of the machinery we have seen at work, interest the visitor. This is the very nursery of ideas, and school of mechanics. We are not surprised to hear that apprentices from the factory have recently taken good Government appointments. The eulogy of a northern engineer was well deserved. The intelligence of the workmen, and their pride in the fame of the house of Miller for mechanical ingenuity, deserve a note of admiration !

A turn brings us to the carpenter's shop and pattern makers' department. Wood models of every description of machinery in work on the premises are stored here. But our attention is attracted to the next shop where is carried on the manufacture of the carriages which convey the bobbins containing the weft threads. The carriage is a triangular plate, with an eye at the top for the thread, a cylindrical centre bore for the bobbin, which is held in its place by an eccentric spring. No less than seventy different operations are required for the manufacture of this single piece of machinery, which to the cursory inspection is a simple, toy-like article. In making the eye of the carriage alone, six distinct processes are needed. In one corner we see the plate being cut, there the eye is being made, here the holes are pierced, and there the spring is being attached to it, with a soldering iron a little larger than a stout pin.

Some twelve years ago the new shops to the right of the entrance, which contain the new locker-roller machines, were erected. Within the last thirty years the fitting shops have been greatly extended, the front portion of the premises have undergone alteration and improvement, the packing operations generally being carried out under altogether changed surroundings. The mills are, for the greater part, fire-proof. The workrooms are heated throughout with hot-water pipes. Ventilating shafts convey away the impure air from each workroom, a Blackman air propeller being employed for this purpose. The houses on the factory side of Vicarage lane are, for the most part, the property of members of the firm, and Derby sends her hundreds to the factory gates daily to earn the wherewithal to buy the daily bread.

III.—THE PILTON GLOVE FACTORY.

Upon the threshold of the glove factory of Messrs. Baylis and Co.—the busy hive of human bees that rears its substantial walls under the shadow of the grey church tower at Pilton—it comes to the visitor as an inspiration that the glamour of romance, the dignity of history, and the pride of antiquity are the inheritance of this industry with a literature. It is not a mere producing-and-distributing, ledger-and-counter business that is about to be described. The old Companies of Glovers, who had souls above sheepskins, gloried in the association of their occupation with antiquity, and interested themselves in its historic lore, its circumstances, and its literature. It is not the purpose of this article to dilate upon the poetry of glove-making, but it is only necessary to take a bird's-eye view of the part this institution—for such it is—has played in civilization to be convinced of the facility with which it lends itself to the art of the romancist. The etymology of gloves is a mystery of itself. Historically, we have gloves in the church, gloves on the throne, gloves on the bench, hawking gloves and gauntlets; symbolically, gloves as pledges, as gages, as gifts, and as favours. Then, as to the antiquity of gloves, Professor Boyd Dawkins, the eminent geologist, tells us—and he would be a bold man who disputed his dictum—that the cave men wore them. An indubitable glove was rudely drawn on a perforated canine, found in Duruthy cave. Pre-historic man lived in the South of France before the glacial period, which commenced—so geologists say—about 240,000 years ago, lasted about 160,000 years, and terminated about 80,000 years since. Here, assuredly, is a respectable antiquity for the glove.

Gloves have played their part in literature. We find Xenophon complaining of the increasing luxury of the Persians, and bringing against them the soft impeachment that they wear " Coverings made of hair for their hands and fingers." Homer, in the *Odyssey*, describes Laertes, the father of Ulysses, in retirement : " While gloves have secured his hands." The Romans were familiar with the glove, and the "shoe" of Scripture—" So he drew off his shoe," in the Book of Ruth— is believed to have referred to the glove. *Hand schuh* (hand shoe) is the picturesque name by which gloves are known in Germany to this day.

It is not alone upon history and social philosophy that the glove has left its mark. [This, as Artemus Ward would say, is no allusion to the P.R.] Proverbial philosophy has enshrined the glove, not for an age, but for all time. It is made to serve both as a complimentary and critical emblem. *Nás troz Cavas,* say the Portuguese,—" He does not wear gloves," *i.e.,* he is a person to be trusted. " Touch not a cat without a glove," our homelier English proverb, is simply a pun on the word Catti, the Teutonic settlers of Cathness, *i.e.,* Catti-ness, and means " Touch not the clan Cattan or Mountain Cat without a glaive." A sermon against dilletanteism is contained in the adage " Cats that go ratting don't wear gloves." " Right as my glove " is an assurance derived from the custom of pledging a glove as the signal of irrefragable faith. " He bit his glove," forboded " he resolved on mortal combat." Then there is the instance where gloves are given to a judge at a maiden assize, when, according to the boy in the street, " nobody has done nothing." It is a polite intimation that the legal dignitary need not come to the bench, but may wear gloves, *i.e.,* take his

ease. To come nearer home, we have the custom three centuries old thus referred to in the Barnstaple Records of
1569-70 : " Paid for a glove for the Fair, 1d." This is one of
many symbolical purposes of the glove. The meaning is that
the fair is established by virtue of the king's glove—the glove
originally conveyed the royal assent. In olden times, a large
glove, decked with dahlias, was suspended from a pole and
protruded from the Quay Hall—then the most ancient building
in Barnstaple—and so remained while the fair lasted. " Thou
knowest the maiden who ventures to kiss a sleeping man wins
of him a pair of gloves," says the glover to Henry Smith, who
had been kissed, as he slept, by fair Catharine, on St. Valen-
tine's morn, in Scott's " Fair Maid of Perth." Henry, in the
next chapter, presents the gloves, and Catherine accepts them.
Thus and thus the pleasing associations of this industry might
be elaborated, but enough has been said for the purpose of this
article.

With the recollection of these attractive associations of the
article with the manufacture of which we are about to make an
acquaintance, the interest is stimulated and the expectation
raised. The Pilton glove factory is a comparatively modern
institution, the centres of the trade in Devon, previous to
1860, being at Torrington and Yeovil. When Mr. J. E. Baylis
—who had previously occupied a responsible position in the
premier glove-making business of England—that house of
world-wide celebrity, Messrs. Dent, Allcroft & Co.—acquired
the compact premises at Pilton, gaiter-making was the principal
feature of the industry then being carried on. A rough, agricultural glove was, however, made for East-country farmers.
Wool-stapling had been the original occupation of the firm of

whose concern Mr. Baylis eventually became the purchaser.
But the factory, before this, had undoubtedly been the seat of
that cloth-trade under the *regime* of which the inhabitants
of Pilton were a prosperous populace. There was a Mayor of
Pilton in the fourteenth century, and a fair was given to it in
the reign of Edward III. In the quaint chronicles of Robert
Incledon, Mayor of Barnstaple in 1735, it is written : " Pilton
is but one fair long street, and is maintained by cloath
making." Ay ! and to the " cloath makers," and to the " cloath
merchants " we owe Pilton Bridge—that is, the original structure. This is how the story runs : " This bridge was made
long since by a merchant of London called Stowford by this
occasion. He chanced to be at Barnstaple to buy cloath and
saw a woman rideing to come over by the low salt marsh
towards Pilton, and the tide came so sudden by a gutt that
breaketh in there from the haven shore to the marsh, that she
could not pass, and crying for help, no man durst come to her,
and so she was drowned. Then Stowford took the Prior of
Barnstaple a certain sum of money to begin this causey checked
on each side, and the bridges, and afterwards paid for the performing it."

It was not surprising that one who had been connected
with the firm that had, more than any other, built up the
British glove trade, should seize the first opportunity of establishing the industry in the new scene of his enterprise. Twenty-
two years ago Mr. Baylis commenced the manufacture of what
are known as doe, buck and dogskin gloves, from the skins of
sheep or lambs. The fact that to-day, counting the in-door and
out-door hands who are employed in the height of the glove-
making seasons, some two hundred wage earners are on the

books of Pilton factory is the best testimonial to the diligence and enterprise with which the business has been conducted, and the success which has crowned the undertaking. Just a year ago Mr. Baylis relieved himself of the more active control of the business, which from that time forth has been in the hands of Messrs. R. E. Gay and A. J. Reavell. The announcement of this arrangement led to a spontaneous expression of respect and goodwill for Mr. Baylis, on the part of the employés, who presented him with an illuminated address.

In describing the markets in which their goods find a ready sale, the firm direct the visitor, after the fashion of Dr. Johnson, to

" Let observation with extensive view
Survey mankind from China to Peru."

Their gloves are distributed by the wholesale London houses, not only throughout the British Isles and Northern Europe, Norway, Sweden and Russia making especial demand for their several manufactures, but in Asiatic Russia, India, North America, and Australia, Pilton Factory gloves may be bought. The house does no retail trade whatever. In dealing with their distribution, before we have described the production of the gloves, the cart has been put before the horse ; but in this case the seeming disarrangement is not without its advantages. Yet, as Mrs. Beeton facetiously informs us in her " Cookery Book," you must catch your hare before you cook it. To the " catching," then.

Before the skins from which the gloves are made reach the factory, they have undergone a preliminary preparation at the hands of the fell-monger. The manufactures of the firm are confined to " oil " and " grain " leather—the signification of

D

which technical terms will appear as we proceed. The sheep-skin, as taken from the back of the animal, has had the wool removed from it by the fell-monger. The " pelts," as the skins are now described, have been immersed in a solution of lime and water for a fortnight. When taken out they are washed and " friezed," and, in the English of the streets, splitted. A " skiver " is then taken off the woolly side, this thin piece of leather being afterwards used for book-binding purposes, or for the lining of " deer-stalker " and other hats. The skin is now placed in " puring " tubs filled with a special preparation, again washed, and next thoroughly beaten in a solution of oil, which gives it that quality of suppleness which so assists in the process of manufacture and is acceptable to the glove wearer. The skin is now " heated," seasoned with a liquid taken from the heating mill, hung up and dried, and taken out into the open air and " staked,"—a process which consists in stretching the skin on a wooden frame and gently operating upon it until it reaches the necessary condition of pliability. The skins, after this operation, are sorted in classes, according to size and quality.

It is in this condition that they are received at the factory ; and, if it be true, as Sir Kenelm Digby has it in his treatise *Of Bodies*, that " We daily see that dogs will have an aversion to glovers that make their ware of dogs' skins ; they will bark at and be churlish to them, and not endure to come near them, though they never saw them before," the canine creation should be respectfully informed that a double dose of original sin belongs to the fell-monger. The glovers of Pilton factory are only " accomplices after the fact." Besides, " dogskin " is but a technical term, now-a-days ; and, though gloves have been made from the molluscous *pinna*, the "silk worm of the sea," so sedulously sought by Sicilian fishermen ; and from "spider silk," of which it takes 700,000 spiders to produce a pound—the sheep's skin is the staple material for glove making. There was a time, however, and not so very long ago, when the stout leathern glove was known as "eighteen-penny-worth of dog."

The foreman of the preparing department of the factory receives the skins and rapidly selects and sorts them, dividing them for the manufacture, respectively, of men's and women's gloves. Inferior skins are set aside and classed as "shammy" (chamois) leather. The second process of preparing is now entered upon. The "oil" leather is first prepared on the flesh side, then immersed in a concoction of cod oil and soap, the oil being "killed" by the mixture of other ingredients. The glover's ideal of soft and supple leather, which enables a good plain, pliable glove, well cut and well made, to be placed in the market, is thus obtained. Our instructor is disposed to follow in the footsteps of "Silas Wegg," and drop into rhyme, as he explains that the time this process occupies "depends upon the leather," and is "according to the weather." From the tub, the skins are taken to a field above the factory, where they are bleached. They next pass through the dyer's hands, and are coloured in various shades of slate and brown, according to order. The kiln in which they are now hung to dry is a primitive institution. Furnaces occupy the floor of the outhouses wherein the skins are hung on nails to the roof and gradually dried. From the kilns they are given out to the workmen who pare, then "stone" them—literally, rub them with a semi-circular tool, faced, in the first instance, with a preparation of emery, and, secondly, with pumice stone. This

D 2

operation produces, what the glover styles, a " fine face " upon
the skin.   Gloves of superior make are re-coloured after this
process ; otherwise, the " oil leather " is ready for the cutter.

The " grain " leather—the sheep's skin which has not been
" split," *i.e.*, the woolly side not having been removed—has gone
through a precisely similar preparation to the " oil " leather up
to the operation of dyeing or tanning.   It has, however, been
subjected to immersion in a mixture of alum and salt before
being despatched to the factory.   A " douse " of hot water is
the warm reception it has at the hands of the foreman of the
preparing department, the skins being plunged in a huge tub
containing water heated to about 80 degrees, according to their
substance.   " Egging " is the euphonious description of the next
process, which is clearly described in the single word.   Placed
in a preparation composed of water and the yolks of eggs, the
skins are " treaded " until they are saturated with the mixture.
Some thousands of gallons of yolk and millions of eggs are
disposed of by glovers in the repetition of this process from
year's end to year's end.   In this condition they are removed
to the kilns, and when dried the skins are " staked," the effect
of which process has been already described.   But a word
must be given to the " parer," whose contribution to the manufacture entails not a little skill and judgment.

A rod with uprights forms the " parer's perch," and his
only tool was described by Shakespeare, in the apt simile,
" With a round beard like a glover's paring knife," which also
lets in a side light upon the few improvements or mechanical
appliances which have assisted the glover up to this stage
of his work.   He attaches the skins as he receives them, one

Plate 5 (above) Tending one of the bottle kilns at Brannam's Barnstaple Pottery; *6 (left)* reconstruction of an old saw pit in St Albans City Museum

Plate 7 *(above)* Fulling stocks similar to those once used at Bradiford Mill and Weare Gifford Fulling Mill; 8 *(below)* unloading timber barges at Rolle Quay Saw Mill, about 1895

by one, to the horizontal beam, and, with a keen-edged quoit-shaped instrument, shaves off the thicker parts of the skin, producing an even surface throughout it. The skins are now ready for the cutter.

Ere we take leave of the preparation department, however, let us gain a bird's-eye view of the rear of the factory in which the operations we have described are carried on. A score of parers' " perches " give an intimation of the number of skins passing through the factory when there is a " rush " in the glove-making trade. Leather lofts, drying rooms, and kilns, together with the yard for " staking " purposes, are compactly enclosed within the premises that extend from the churchyard steps back to the wool-stapling lofts of the Messrs. Spurway. The whole of the buildings in the rear, including the cutters' room, machine rooms, etc., have been added since the advent of Mr. Baylis. In summer, old Sol does the glove-making industry a " good turn," the warmth communicated by his rays dispensing, for the greater part, with the necessity for the artificial heat of the kilns.

With the receipt of the skins from the preparing room by the foreman cutter commences the glove-making proper. Experience has taught this skilled operative the kind of glove for the manufacture of which each skin is best adapted, and the number of pairs which it is capable of producing. He receives his orders from the counting-house of the firm, and proceeds to put them in hand by issuing the leather to the cutters. A ticket which he gives out with the skins contains the instructions to the cutter. When it is remembered that upon the skill and accuracy of the cutter depends, not only the fit of the gloves, but the use of the material to its best advantage,

the importance of the next process is understood. It is not his
work to imitate the tailor's cutter in fashioning the " cut " of
the garment. A pair of scissors is his only tool. He has to
cut the leather into " tranks " (pieces) of the requisite length
and width for the manufacture of the different parts of the
glove. He first draws down or "tries out " to its utmost the
leather at the side of his cutting-table, thus securing that
all the surface of the " tranks " shall be equal in elasticity.
Then, swiftly and smartly, his experienced eye his only guide,
he divides the skin to the best advantage. The tranks, welts,
thumb-pieces, and fourchettes—the various pieces of the
glove—are now forwarded to the punching department, where
they are reduced to the shape which they will take in the
manufactured glove. Immediately the visitor gets a sight of
the punch in the shape of a hand, the process which the glover
has mystified with the term of " webbing " becomes the best
understood operation of the industry. We have seen how the
thumb-piece, the quirks, the fourchettes inserted between the
fingers, and the wrist welt are cut out separately. Now two
pairs of tranks are placed upon the wooden slide which
contains the punch or knife shaped in the form of a hand ; a
gutta-percha block is then laid on the tranks, the whole is slid
underneath the press, and with two turns of the wheel the
punching or slitting is completed. When the block is taken ont
of the press the leather is seen neatly cut in the shape of an
open glove. The thumbs and fourchettes are slit with smaller
punches. From the presses the pieces pass to the " sizer," who
stamps the size and number on them, and ties them in bundles
of six pairs. They are next received by the forewoman of the
sewing department, who examines them before issuing them to
the glove-makers.

The first stage is that of pointing the back of the trank with silk cord and feather stitching. This is done by machine hands, and is equivalent to the scroll stitching on the knuckles which was a fantastic feature of the glove of the middle ages. " Raising," Imperial and Paris stitching, and " spearing," the latter done by hand, are styles of ornamental workmanship in which the deft-fingered women of the factory are expert. Spearing is done in a heavy class of men's driving gloves, the spear head finishing the pointing. Bicycle gloves with perforated backs, the perforation being filled with coloured crochet work, remind us of the golden circles on the gloves of William of Wykeham. In pointing, the ends are left untied by the machinists, and a row of younger girls, known as "end-tiers," are employed in pulling out, knotting, and snipping the thread-ends—a work which they briskly get through at a high rate of speed.

A flight of stairs brings us to what is pre-eminently the glove-making department. A whirr as of many wheels greets us, and forty sewing machines, of a type specially manufactured for gloving purposes, are seen working as one. The different machinists are variously engaged, here sewing in the fourchettes, there adding the thumb-pieces, now closing backs and palms, then facing finger to finger, until the glove is complete. So Pelham, who would have three tradesmen make his gloves— " one for the hand, a second for the fingers, and a third for the thumb "—might have been accommodated after all. Disraeli, in the days of dalliance, when he sparked it with "the wealthy curled darlings of our nation," exceeded this measure of foppery by wearing gloves of white kid with long-hanging fringes of black silk at the wrists. "Setting-on," "thumbing," "welting," and " closing " are the technical terms employed by the hands who are daily fashioning the fabric in this lofty, light, and well-ventilated room. Two forewomen have charge of the department One gives out and takes in the work, and the other examines it as it comes from the machinists' hands.

In one instance, that of the D'Orsay glove—doubtless named after the handsome beau who set the fashion in the eighteenth century—it is lined at the factory and stitched through, with a pricked seam. But, for the greater part, the lining of the gloves is done by out-door hands. The allusion to D'Orsay has brought to our recollection the strange story told by Athenæus of a celebrated glutton who always came to table habited in gloves, so that he might be able to handle and eat the meat while hot, and thus devour more than the rest of the company. Singular to relate, this tale of the gourmand is preserved to us in the description of a particular class of gloves—" Men's Gold Tan Glutton."

In the ordinary course the work is issued to the out-door employés—former factory hands for the most part—from the wareroom adjoining the department last described. To six pairs of gloves an equal number of linings are added, the parcel is ticketed, and the "liner" takes it from the hand of the workwoman who will by-and-bye receive the lined gloves. It was not this kind of "lining," but one of a more metallic character, to which Sir Thomas More took exception in the sixteenth century. Mrs. Croaker had presented the upright judge with a pair of gloves lined with forty pounds in "angels" as a "token" from a grateful suitor who had won her cause before him. "Mistress," quaintly wrote the Lord Chancellor of that day, "since it were against good manners to receive your gift, I am content to take your glove, but as for the lining I utterly refuse."

With button-holing, buttoning and topping—double-needle sewing round the wrist of the glove—the process of "finishing" is completed. In olden times gloves were "topped" with narrow ribands of various colours and textures, with gold and silver interwoven. From the "finisher" the gloves have gone to the examiner—where any slight defect is remedied, and a flagrant fault traced to its source—ere they have reached the ironing room. The "unshaped" glove is here stretched upon a hot iron hand and is fashioned to the shapely form in which the insinuating draper offers it to his customer as "a thing of beauty." In days of old, when beaus were bold, some super-fine exquisites had their gloves made on prepared models of their hands—really hand lasts. Deposited upon the table of the pairer,—the matchmaker of the glove trade, who has, happily, to deal with less ill-assorted couples that humanity wots of—the gloves are paired up, tacked together, banded according to order, boxed, and passed on to the packer, who despatches them to the wholesale houses.

A little yellow ticket has accompanied the glove through-out its peregrinations, and has enabled it to be traced wherever glove or glove-makers go astray. Each glove passes through more than thirty hands, and, on an average, 3,000 stitches are inserted in it. At least 200 different varieties, distinct in character or in some matter of detail, are made at Pilton factory from time to time. Just now the Astrachan glove—woolly cloth and black and coloured leather—is in great

demand ; it is wholly of home manufacture.   Having followed
the glove from its rough state in the tranks to its finish, when,
" an immaculate fit," it is on its way to the wholesale house,
we are at liberty to look about us and note some of the etceteras of the manufacture carried on in this block of buildings,
three stories high, which the Factory Inspector has pronounced
almost a model of what such premises should be.   Leaving the
" placing-up room," from whence the glove whose manufacture
we have watched is launched upon its trading travels, we
interest ourselves in the hooking and eye-letting process, which
is an alternative for buttoning and button-holing.

Side by side with this operation, the matching and uniting
of gloves and gauntlets is going on, and at the word " gauntlet "
imagination calls up the picture of the Teutonic mediæval
knight throwing it down as a challenge, using these words :
Dat is min glove ! (That is my belief).

In the lofty warerooms, silks and cottons, buttons and
linings are stacked.   According to the vagaries of fashion,
gloves have from two to sixteen buttons.   The ladies of this
enlightened century—by the way, the softer sex were late in
adopting gloves—are, however, by no means so extravagant as
their sisters of the sixteenth century.   In the *Progresses of
Queen Elizabeth*, for instance, Nicholls quotes among the
" gifts "—" By the Lady Mary Grey, ij peir of swete (perfumed)
gloves with *fower dozen buttons* of golde, in every one a side
perle."   The Lady Mayoress of London, 1887, was presented
with long undressed kid gloves, embellished with no less than
twenty buttons

Among the separate processes appertaining to particular

makes of gloves, that by which the "Tilbury'd" driving glove
is produced will be most interesting to the reader. The leather
is doubled under the three "rein fingers," the friction in driving
being thus anticipated.. Glove linings are cut in the punching
room upstairs with a fixed knife, a thumb-screw regulating the
sizes. The cloth of which the "glove of the day" is manufactured originally came, as its name indicates, from the back of
the sheep of the far-off region of Astrachan. The sheep skins
used in the ordinary manufactures are drawn from various
countries of Europe, and in large quantities from the Cape
Colony. Lamb skins, so extensively used now-a-days, are
bought in Russia, in Europe, Italy, Turkey, Servia, Spain,
Asia Minor, Arabia, Persia and South America. Messrs.
Baylis & Co. supply the wholesale house with a special article
—a men's winter driving glove for which they claim the distinction of its being the warmest lined glove in the trade.
These gloves are made of real slinks—lamb skins, dyed on the
woolly side, the palms being of buck or grain leather. Slates,
fawns and browns are the colours in which their ordinary glove
trade lies.

In the front of the premises are the counting-house, warerooms, and packing department of the business. The buildings
in the rear were altered, and, to some extent, newly-erected by
Mr. Baylis, when the glove factory was removed from its
original site to the scene of the present busy manufactory.
Though Pilton has lost somewhat of its pristine glory as a
manufacturing centre, in its glove factory it possesses an industry which, from its extent, the enterprise manifested in its
management, and the skill and interest of the trade, is no
mean boast. To the pessimist who sighs for "the good old

days " of the woollen manufactures, we may commend the truism which has universal application, " There's nothing like leather," which Sir Edwin Arnold has now, in his graceful, half-pathetic lines to an ancient Egyptian slipper, done into rhyme :

> Leather will last
> When loves and delights and beautiful things
> Have vanished forgotten.

The making of the Pilton factory glove has been described by us. The talented author of the " Light of Asia " has prophesied its fame in the survival of the fittest of industries.

IV.—THE BARUM WARE FACTORY.

Beyond and above the other industries of the capital of North Devon, the productions of the Royal Barum Ware Pottery have conferred public distinction upon Barnstaple. In Art circles, Mr. Charles H. Brannam, the creator of this artistic industry, has been awarded " an honourable place in the list of England's original ceramists." Wherever his taste, industry and enterprise, and the attractive designs of his accomplished decorators, have made a market for the ware, Barum and North Devon have been honoured by association with the most ancient of arts in the brilliant revival of its former glory. It is difficult to rightly appraise the privilege of connection with an industry whose history extends beyond the purview of written record, and an art whose beauty is inherent, without laying ourselves open to the charge of exaggeration ; but where the commercial spirit has not yet destroyed all inborn feeling for fine art and beauty, and there still exists a regard for antique objects and trades which are,

so to speak, fossilized history, we shall be rightly understood
in setting a high value upon the fact that there flourishes in
Barnstaple to-day an art industry for the date of whose birth
we must go to pre-historic remains, and whose beauty and high
place among the decorative arts have been exalted in our
midst.

It is conducive to a just estimation of the interest of the
industry we are about to notice to remember that, to all
intents and purposes, the art of the potter to-day and his
tools are precisely the same as those of the Egyptian, who
toiled at the potter's wheel about 4,000 years B.C.,—just 6,000
years ago—as is shewn by existing fragments of pottery.
Among the prized examples of form in the local School of Art
is a vase which boasts the respectable antiquity of some 3,000
years.   The potter has figured in classic and sacred literature.
Homer compared the rhythm of a dance to the spin of a
potter's wheel, and the prophet Jeremiah employs the type of
a potter to illustrate God's absolute power in disposing of
nations : " Then I went down to the potter's house, and,
behold, he wrought a work on the wheels.   And the vessel
that he made of clay was marred in the hand of the potter ; so
he made it again another vessel, as seemed good to the potter
to make it."— JEREMIAH xviii., 3-4.

In North Devon itself pottery has attained to an age that
commands respect.   An eminent archæologist has traced its
history back over 1,500 years to "Abertawe" and the
"Artavia" of the Romans, with which Barnstaple has been
identified.   Mr. Earle Way introduced the subject to the
Archæological Society in 1879, with a paper on "The survival

of ancient Roman types of pottery at Barnstaple," pointing out the peculiarities and extreme antiquity of the Barnstaple potteries. The original designation of Cross Street is a link in the chain of evidence establishing the historical prestige of Barum potteries. From time immemorial, says a local historian, it was called Crok Street, which was sometimes varied to Crokke Street. It was so described in the earliest deeds, from 1331, and in the church documents of 1507 and subsequently. In later deeds and in a rental of 1633 it was modernised to Crock Street, the corruption to Cross Street being comparatively recent. The original name was held to have commemorated the potter's art, which was, it was added, a staple trade from a very early era, and largely practised in the town and neighbourhood. Elizabethan, as well as previous, bye-laws ordained that no potter, baker, or brewer should set up any furze ricks within the town, except on certain conditions, and Crock Street was especially set apart for exposing pottery for sale—perhaps for manufacture. Thus, there is irrefragable proof that the local manufacture of ware has been continuous for 550 years.

Of the curious evidences of antiquity and of local association which have received attention, there could scarcely be any more interesting or illustrative than the names given to the various sizes of pitchers and the odd custom of counting them. There is no mistaking the fact that the following descriptions are decided localisms : " Long Tom," " Ferret-tail," " Gully-mouth," " Pinch-gut," " Sixties," and " Penny Joogs.' The names are given in the order of the pitchers, from the largest to the smallest. Then, again, there are "land" dozens and "sea" dozens of Barum ware, and, strangest of all, the former consists of thirty-nine and the latter of sixty! Sixty to a "dozen"—but a trade "dozen," of course.

For more than five centuries past pottery has, therefore, undoubtedly been one of the industries of Barnstaple. The Borough Records contain numerous entries referring to potters and their practices—not always commendable, alas! for it would appear that the Barum potter (of the past, of course), was, in more than ordinary measure, a "dry, thirsty soul,"— presumably on account of his occupation. The very existence of Potter's Lane, on the North Walk, in close contiguity to Brannam's pottery, has its own important bearing upon the question of the existence of the industry in Barnstaple over a long term of years. Fragments of 15th and 16th century Barum ware, which have been dug up in the locality, are preserved by art connoisseurs of the neighbourhood. The name "Barum," which appears upon them, disposes of all conjectures. Many very curious and early specimens are in museums, and the Fort Hill and Castle excavations brought to light numerous remains of pottery.

The Litchdon Street Pottery, which is the peculiar home of Barum art ware, was in the possession of a potter named Lovering toward the end of the eighteenth century. A Mr. Rendle worked the Strand pottery, where Potter's Pill and Potter's Strand once described familiar spots, before the dawn of the nineteenth century. The Litchdon Street and North Walk potteries have now been carried on under one management for some sixty years. Messrs. Rendle & Son was the "style and name" of the original firm. In their employment, Mr. Brannam, sen., worked as a journeyman. He afterwards acquired a 14 years' lease of the North Walk pottery from the Rendles, and, seven or eight years later, an opportunity of purchasing the Litchdon Street pottery presenting itself, Mr. Brannam, sen., acquired it, and thus became the proprietor of both.

The most interesting object associated with the North Walk pottery may have some bearing on the antiquity of the art in Barnstaple. In the first of the row of cottages in Potter's Lane, which are owned by Mr. Brannam, there is a well preserved coat of arms over the mantelpiece in one of the bedrooms, and a scroll, here and there hidden by the persistent efforts of the Philistine " lime-washer," in keeping, both in the style of the seventeenth century. On either side of the coat of arms are figures upholding emblems, and the date 1675, together with the initials " I B," " A B," " C B." It is surmised that the coat of arms may have been that of a potters' guild, and the emblems, which are unfortunately effaced, designatory of the art. Some of the cottages formerly belonged to " the lords and ladies of Pilton." The old works abutted on the present Strand Road, the open kiln used in those days being fired with furze. " Oven tiles " were largely shipped to Ireland.

The manufacture of art ware in Barnstaple owes its origin to one of those singular occurrences which we are oft inclined to look upon as pleasant fictions. There is little doubt but that, however it came about, the present prominence of Barum ware in the market as decorative work, for the beautification of English homes, was assured from the moment Mr. Charles H. Brannam, the present proprietor of the North Devon Art Pottery, entered the Barnstaple School of Art as a student.

But years before the industry had its inception. The potters, as they took their meals by the side of their silent wheels, would shape the plastic clay into odd objects ; and their employer of that day, noticing some affinity between the figures modelled by the men and the grotesque productions of the ancients, caused the more striking of them to be "fired." They caught the attention of affluent townsmen, for whom sets of ware, with these rustic decorations, were manufactured.

The Great Exhibition of 1851, to which many an industry, then in its infancy, owes that fillip which gave it something more than "a local habitation and a name," saw the first specimens of Sgraffiato ware sent out from the Barum potteries. Sgraffiato ware, it may be well to explain, is made by covering a vessel of red clay (terra cotta) with a coating of white slip made of some natural white earth, like pipe-clay. This is done by dipping or by pouring the fluid-slip over the red vessel. When the white coating is dry, the design is formed by cutting it away so as to expose the red body underneath. The patterns are picked out with bright colours, and, finally, the whole is glazed. Half-a-dozen jugs decorated after this fashion were sent to the Great Exhibition of '51 by Mr. Brannam, sen. A bronze medal was awarded them, and Prince Albert himself complimented the potter on the skill evinced in their production.

For the greater part, however, Barum ware was still of an ordinary description—"a sound and useful, but not an artistic pottery." Drains and roofing tiles, pots and pans, were the "lines" in which the business ran. But, with the advent of Mr. Charles Brannam in the pottery, the introduction of art work only became a question of time and opportunity. The

E

proud position attained by Barum ware in the art world may justly be ascribed to the strong artistic feeling developed by Mr. Brannam in the School of Art. His first essay was in small jugs and vases of ordinary shapes—Sgraffiato ware, as we have described it, in its simplest forms. In 1880, Mr. Brannam was fortunate enough to attract the attention of one of the partners of the well-known firm of Messrs. Howell and James, who is a Devonshireman, to the ware. A few of Mr. Brannam's earlier attempts were taken by him to London, where they were shown to Mr. J. Buxton Morrish, another partner in the same firm. According to an art writer who has done justice to the beauty of form and excellence in design of the ware, " Mr. Morrish at once divined the talent and originality latent in the rough but artistic designs, and sent down his manager to Barnstaple to make definite proposals to Mr. Brannam—to assist him in developing his new ware, and to become his sole representative in London. Shortly after this Mr. Brannam visited London, where he conferred with Mr. Morrish, whose taste and experience were, I believe, of much value in suggesting variations as to shape and colour." Professor Church next gave the new industry an impetus. He was delivering his series of Cantor Lectures on artistic pottery at the Society of Arts, and took occasion to bring some specimens of Barum ware before his audience. The distinguished R. A. remarked : " Mr. Brannam is now producing some fine vases in the peculiarly quaint and original style which he has made his own, coloured with glazes of flowing and pulsating hues. The bold foliage-work and the grotesque animal forms which decorate this ' Barum ware,' remind one at once of the rare Italian graffiato ware and of some of the quaintest and rarest English and Staffordshire productions of the seventeenth century." With the encouragement of appreciative art critics as an incentive to renewed effort, Mr. Brannam developed the artistic side of his manufactures, and in a laudatory notice of that day it was recorded that he had "not only set his inventive faculty to work in producing many excellent and novel designs, but had greatly extended the range and improved the quality of his colours." The history of the pottery since Mr. Brannam acquired it, by inheritance, seven years since, is one uninterrupted chronicle of progress. By the employment of Messrs. Dewdney & Baron, skilled designers, the character of the decoration has been enhanced, whilst added variety has been given to the shapes and increased beauty to the glazes by Mr. Brannam himself.

In 1886 the row of cottages and warehouses, contiguous to the pottery in Litchdon Street, gave place to an exceedingly handsome and attractive block of buildings. Upon the shop window and entrance artistic treatment was lavished with a liberal hand, and Barum ware was exhibited in an attractive setting. In the imposing porch entrance to the shop, the now celebrated ware was introduced in pillars of elaborate workmanship ; the standels of the windows being filled with it, and columns of ware inserted in the windows, while a string of it appeared below the second floor windows.

The alterations were not confined to the beautified front, the artistic appearance of which continues to attract admiring attention, but extended to the pottery and store rooms in the rear. But we will enter, and, while we inspect the commodious warerooms, make a point of investigating the simple, yet delicate operations of the potter which ever and anon produce "a thing of beauty."

E 2

On the left, as we enter the pottery, is the primitive " pug " or mill, in which the clay is mixed and ground. The clay comes from the Fremington pits, which are largely worked in summer, the year's supply having to be provided whilst a genial atmosphere prevails, winter not permitting the clay to be dug out, and consequently stopping the supplies. Carted to the mill house, the common brick clay and that used in the manufacture of pitchers is mixed with sand from Braunton Burrows, and ground down to the necessary plasticity in the mill, which is worked by a horse that sleepily paces its wearying, monotonous round. Clay for the ware is prepared in a smaller " hand-pug " at the top of the pottery yard, where the white clay for "slips" is also stored. This is beaten, chopped, and freed from gravel before it is employed, as a fluid, in the manufacture of Sgraffiato ware.

Commencing at the lowest round of the potter's ladder, a word or two may be written descriptive of brick making. The simile of making bricks without straw appears to have lost its point, for we fail to detect the presence of cornstalks in the plastic mould of the Barum brick. The potter fills his brick-mould with clay, scrapes the surface, lays the shaped brick upon a wood carrier, on which it is taken to the drying-place by a boy in attendance on the brick maker. The manufacture of roofing-tiles and drain-pipes requires a little more ingenuity. Pipes are made with machinery of a rude but effectual type. A quantity of clay is placed in the receiver of a long cylindrical chamber, at one end of which there is a travelling screw, styled the "driver," and at the other end a rounded opening of the circumference and thickness of the pipe to be manufactured. The "driver" forces

the clay through the orifice, and the pipe protrudes outside,
where it is received on a roller and carried out to the desired
extent, when the pipe, in its soft state, is cut by lifting
a wire arrangement under the rollers, and thus divided into
the requisite lengths. The drains are then slightly hardened
by exposure, and afterwards shaped by the insertion of wooden
rollers, with which the rounded appearance that characterises
them when they have left the kilns is obtained. Bricks
and drain-pipes, though most useful, are rather prosaic articles,
and it is with an accession of interest that we turn to the
potter at his wheel. Boys have made the clay from the mill
yet more plastic by "working" it, very much after the fashion
that cook kneads her dough, and then, a perfectly homogeneous
mass, in the language of the potter the pot is thrown by the
aid of a very simple contrivance consisting of a small round
table fixed on a revolving pivot. The ease with which the
plastic clay answers to the touch of the hand and rises or
falls, taking a whole succession of symmetrical shapes, and
seeming, as it were, instinct with the life and thought of
the potter, as an admiring writer has well said, makes the
art beautiful and striking above all others. At the sight of
the potter,—the facility and deftness of his movements, the
suppleness of his fingers, the simplicity of his tools, and the
beauty, ease and grace of his work,—our thoughts are carried
back on the tide of time to the flow of the Art impulse, when
the Egyptian fellaheen, on the banks of sacred Nile, practised
the same storied art. We see the shapeless mass of clay
gradually grow into a large pot, which, though a common
piece of ware, is not without beauty for the seeing eye in
its symmetrical shape. In its " dough " state, the pot is taken

to the drying-house. Here the "finishing off" process is carried on. The workman who is, in technical language, said to be "grinding the metal," is really keeping in condition the glaze which is applied to the inside of pots and pitchers. After it has been glazed, the pot will, by-and-bye, be removed to the kiln, for the making of pottery actually depends on the chemical change that takes place when the clay is heated in the fire.

Art critics have bemoaned the use of the mould in English pottery, subversive, as it is, of all originality and really artistic work. Barum ware is all thrown—manufactured on the wheel—hence its merits as art work. There are exceptions, of course, but these, it will appear, are the consequences of shape and size.

Everyone must have noticed, with more or less curiosity as to the cause, the triangular mark at the bottom of all decorative ware. This is the explanation : finer work, when ready for the kiln, is packed in "seggers," *i.e.*, in fire clay cases, protecting them from undue pressure. The pots are placed in the "seggers" on "spurs," little triangular clay rests that raise them from the surface of the "segger." It is these little rests that "make their mark." Much skill is bestowed on kiln-laying, and the object which the workman has in view, though he may give it another name, is really "the survival of the fittest." First, there are three or four layers of bricks, then a layer of pans, whilst around them are piles of pitchers. Touching the sides are kiln-pipes, which admit of the heat and flame passing through. The " seggers " containing vases are placed in the centre : they stand on " spurs," as has been explained, to prevent their adhering to the "seggers." The kiln, when ready, is a very solid structure. Tapering toward the top, it has a broad superstructure, around which ware is placed in the first stage. The kiln having been "soaked"—partially heated for a week, it is fired and is kept burning for two days and nights, a similar period being allowed it to cool.

Now that we have followed the common ware to its completion, let us enumerate some of the more interesting products of the pottery in this direction. The bread oven, indigenous to the soil of Devon and Cornwall, and "made by the peck," is here in all sizes, and awakens the keen demands of appetite for the sweet wheaten bread baked in these ovens by the thrifty farmers' wives of the sister counties. Through serried rows of pans and pitchers, stains and butter pots, baking dishes and collanders, pipkins and preserve pots, salting pans and bread pans, tongue pans and harvest pans,—not a few of them rich in colour and comely in form ; flower pots *galore*, stump trees, seakale pots, garden tiles, orchid pots, creases, hyacinth pots, rhubarb pots, rustic pots, and glazed stoneware, we pick our delicate way, ere we get a glimpse of the department in which the finer art ware is produced by skilled workmen, and the fame of the house is being built up..

The finer ware is all "thrown" by Mr. Brannam himself, and the beautifully proportioned vases that have justly earned artistic compliment indicate how close and accurate a student of form the proprietor of the pottery is, and to what perfection he has personally attained in the art. The vase having been "thrown," it is prepared for the decorator. In the decorating room we find the firm's designers who have attained considerable distinction in local and county art circles by their exhibits. Messrs. Dewdney and Baron, who have been associated with the Barum ware pottery for, respectively, seven and four years past, are assisted by apprentices. The designer completes the decoration of a vase, and the more crucial portion on each succeeding pot, the apprentices working out the details of his ideas, and thus gaining excellent training in design. The principal portion of the decorative work is in sgraffiato. The design is etched direct upon the pot, there being no previous working out of it on paper. The vase is received in its "green state;" the backgrounds are then taken out, the surface being scraped away. Great variety is obtained by these simple methods. Much of the distinction which causes vases of precisely similar design to differ materially from each other is due to the operation of "firing." Two pots going into different kilns, or even into different parts of one kiln, will invariably present great dissimilarity in their finished state, the ware being materially affected by the heat to which it is subjected. More recently, the very effective *Pate sur Pate* treatment of the vases has, to some extent, replaced the earlier styles of Barum ware. "Slip upon slip," applied work, as distinct from the etched work of the sgraffiato, fairly describes this process. The "slip" is painted upon the body of the vase. Although the range of the colourist is confined to only half-a-dozen colours, yet some thirty or forty tints are obtained by means of mixture and in the "firing." The "slips" are produced with coloured liquid clays. Into the secrets of their manufacture and the production of the glazes we are forbidden to enter; indeed, our guide, who has been the most communicative of cicerones hitherto, is suddenly metamorphosed into the jealous custodian of treasured knowledge. "Who steals my vase, steals little," he, says in effect, "but he who filches from me the secrets of my art robs me of that which not enriches him and makes me poor indeed." We forbear from further prying into the prison house of the soul of the potter's craft, and are rewarded for our forbearance by an introduction to some choice examples of Barum ware.

The designs, it is pointed out to us, consist of panels of various forms sympathising with the shapes of the vessels, and filled with conventionalised birds, fishes, and foliage. The entire series are marked by much fertility of invention and decorative ingenuity. There is no moulding, no representation of stereotyped ideas : the designer is an artist, and with the enthusiasm of one who loves his work for the work's sake, he ever and again presents us with some new thing—the production of his fertile brain, guided by his invariable good taste and the canons of true art. The panels are separated by bold scrolls and zigzags, and the corners and odd places filled with globes, shells and other plain and effective forms. This was held to give the earlier productions of the pottery " an individuality of a somewhat archaic character, as though an early Egyptian potter had transmitted his simple artistic feeling to his successor in Devon." The Italian Renaissance style has monopolised the later work of the pottery and has not suffered by comparison with its previous achievements. A word of the colours. The owner of the Royal Barum Pottery has discovered the way to make and use the thickly-glazed blues and greens of the old Persian ware. Since it was said of Mr. Brannam, as an original ceramist, that, in addition to the contrasts of white and red and bronze and yellow, with which

he first started, he had produced very soft and rich com-
binations of chocolate and blue, leaf-green and pale yellow, and
other secondaries and tertiaries, his inventive genius has made
some valuable additions to the glazes.

Passing from the decorator's department to the show-room
of the pottery in the front, we can trace the successive achievements of Mr. Brannam and his assistants in shape and design.
In bottles and vases, fruit dishes and baskets, salad bowls,
biscuit jars, cheese dishes, salts, flower pots, butter dishes,
knives and forks, umbrella stands, and a variety of other forms
to which plastic clay lends itself, Barum ware may now
be obtained. But we give that special attention which is their
due to the larger vases in which the skill of the potter and the
art of the designer have finest expression. Here, for instance,
is that masterpiece of the potter's art, a symmetrically-pro-
portioned vase, over three feet in height, thrown in one piece,
which was such a conspicuous exhibit at the recent County
Show ; approaching the great Greek vase in height, with its
glazes of those " flowing and pulsating hues " for which the
Barum ware early gained the admiration of the artist, and the
quaint Japanese design, it deservedly has prominent mention
in our catalogue. Then there are Egyptian vases, with
designs, in panels, after nature, and in keeping with the
beautiful shape of the vessel, executed in lightish blue and
dark green upon a brown ground ; Persian designs in blue and
white ; Greek vases, appropriately distinguished for the purity
of their form ; and Japanese pots, with conventional decorations, to be mentioned before we have even hinted at the
variety of shape and design which characterises the magnificent show of vases.

There are no pretensions to chronological order in this
series of articles, and the sequence of the story of the progress
of the art industry of Barnstaple will rather be maintained
than departed from in taking our leave of the pottery with
some references to the distinctions which have been conferred
upon the ware and its manufacturer in recent years. First
and foremost, in the year 1885, Her Majesty the Queen patron-
ized the pottery, the work of which was henceforth entitled to
the description of Royal Barum Ware. The Sovereign has not
been alone in her patronage of the ware, as other scions of
Royalty may be numbered among its purchasers. Prize medals
have been awarded Mr. Brannam's exhibits at County Shows
in Bodmin, Exeter, and Newton. The Royal Cornwall Poly-
technic Society conferred its coveted medal upon the North
Devon ceramist. When the contract with Messrs. Howell and
James, mentioned in the earlier history of the pottery, terminated, the London firm would have renewed it, but Mr. Brannam preferred to be unhampered ; and now, in addition to
Messrs. Howell and James, Messrs. Liberty, the celebrated
art furnishers, and other noted London houses, act as agents
for the sale of the ware. Messrs. Jones, of Lynton, and Glyde,
of Ilfracombe, make extensive sales of it to tourists in the
season, and throughout the larger towns of the United Kingdom Mr. Brannam is now represented. Mr. Owen Davies, the
eminent designer, who suggested the development of the ware
to Mr Brannam, from time to time exhibits his continued
interest in the progress of the industry. Mr. Ernest Radford,
LL.M., in the course of his lectures on Art, under the Univer-
sity Extension system, last year paid a high compliment to the
artistic value of the ware, and Sir Philip Cunliffe-Owen,

Director of the South Kensington Museum, who visited the
pottery on the occasion of his presence in the town for the
purpose of distributing the prizes to the students of the School
of Art, has since shewn that he maintains the high esteem he
then expressed for the beauty and value of the ware as an art
production. The finely modelled figure (by Mr. Baron) in
Rock Park was a unique example of the capabilities of the
pottery, and with the mention of this *magnum opus* we may
fitly conclude a most gratifying chronicle of the achievements
of a citizen who, in advancing his own interests, has conferred
great distinction upon his native town, and given to Art one
more triumph and enduring monument.

V.—SAW AND TURNING MILLS.

In a pause between our descriptions of the larger and
better known industries of Barnstaple, and before we enter
upon the wider commercial field outside the capital of North
Devon, it may not be uninteresting nor unprofitable to direct
attention to two minor undertakings which, though they employ no great amount of labour, are yet indicative of that
growth in proportion and mechanical progress which have
already been alluded to as gratifying characteristics of the
modern industries of this division of the county. In the saw-
mill of Messrs. Rawle, Gammon, and Baker, and Messrs.
Mountjoy and Hancock's Bradiford turning mill, we shall also
find further examples of the variety of commercial enterprise
and diversity of occupation which still entitle Barnstaple
to something of its ancient reputation as a manufacturing
centre. There is a certain affinity between the two businesses

about to be noticed which justifies their being grouped together in one article. Messrs. Rawle, Gammon, and Baker, timber merchants, confine their attention to the raw material, whilst at the Bradiford mill Messrs. Mountjoy and Hancock are engaged in turning trees into brush backs—the wood in the rough into japanned heads and handles for the brush manufacturer proper.

ROLLE'S QUAY STEAM SAW MILLS.

Observing the sequence of the industries, then, we call upon Messrs. Rawle, Gammon, and Baker at their new offices, whose septagonal front commands the traffic from their timber yard, the Quay, Rolle Street, and (across the Drawbridge) the ends of High Street and Boutport Street. Progress has set its imprimatur upon the very threshold of their enterprise, for where we are standing is the site of that once familiar land-mark, the "old saw pit," in which, for thirty years, "top-sawyer," and "pit-man" carried on their laborious operations. Five-and-thirty years ago the business was established by Messrs. Samuel Rawle and William Gammon. The present Mr. Gammon succeeded to the concern by inheritance, and nine years since was joined in partnership by Mr. Baker. It is within the last decade that the development of the mill has gone on, and the past few years have seen the enterprise of the firm at its high water mark. Six cottages, extending along the Rolle Street boundary of the timber yard, have been built, a drying-store erected, and the front of the premises completed with the recent addition of the smart suite of offices. It is worthy of remark that in the handsome interior arrangements of the offices the firm's matchboarding has been employed with most satisfactory results. But our mission to-day is not so much to familiarize ourselves with the excellent accommodation which has been provided for the transaction of the clerical portion of the business. This has already been described, and it remains for us to investigate the industrial side of the undertaking. A word must be given in passing, however, to the substantially-built modern wood store next the offices in Rolle Street, where the important " deals " and " boards," consigned from Norwegian, Swedish, Archangel, and American ports, are stored. The masonry of this store, for which Mr. William Garland, of Boutport Street, is responsible, has received the honourable distinction of being classed among the best examples of constructive work in the town. The building is designed on the newest principle, in which fast and thorough drying is assisted by the introduction of improvements which experience has suggested.

The foreigner—who is the *bête noire* of the commercial Englishman just now—has, with his primeval forests, inexhaustible supplies, cheap labour, and facilities for export, " cut us out " in several branches of the trade. For instance, in " planed boarding " he can supply the English merchant with wood " in yard " infinitely cheaper than the home market will permit the English article to be purchased.   Consolation may, however, be derived from the fact, that " moulds " and " skirting," with which the "furriner " used to flood the market, can now—thanks to the development of our British mechanical genius—be done on the spot to the exercise of economy.

" What is the history of the wood before it reaches Barnstaple ? " That is an interesting question, and as the reply will explain how an important branch of the trade of the Port of Barnstaple is carried on, it is worth while to give it *in extenso*. Hewn in the forests of Northern Europe and America the wood passes from the saw-mill to the sea. The terrible history of that huge timber raft which, rent asunder by the storm, drifted helplessly, dangerously, hither and thither, on the great transatlantic river, vividly illustrated the ways and means of timber exportation. The imports of Messrs. Rawle, Gammon, and Baker, are shipped in vessels of six hundred tons burden, whose charter shows their destination to be Appledore Pool. From the Pool, where the great timber ships are always afloat, the cargo is conveyed in barges up the Taw to Rolle's Quay and the timber yard of the firm, which, when the tide is high, is, for a third of its extent, submerged. " With a yo, heave O ! " you may hear the jolly lumber-men unshipping a barge's load on the top of the tide, some moon-light night, when Rawle, Gammon, and Baker's yard is the scene of the greatest activity.

Fancy match-boarding, now so largely employed in office, house, and public building, is largely stored here, beside the odorous yellow pine boards, and rich-hued mahogany. The store-room is open underneath for drying purposes, the free play of air about the wood facilitating its quick seasoning. But this principle is generally and yet more effectively applied to the newest store of the firm, next in the order of the premises to the offices. This building is of a unique description, promoting, as it does, a continuous movement of air about the wood stored in it. It is erected for the special purpose of drying the best quality "Archangel deals," a cargo of which has just been discharged and admirably stored in the improved shed, which,

while it admits of the free passage of air, is still a shelter
against the rain.   The masonry is of local brick (Messrs.
Lauder and Smith's), and the designs and nature of the
structure have commended themselves to the judgment of
experts.   Provision is made for storing from two to three
hundred tons.

The old wooden store, on our right, and next the drawbridge, will be the next "institution" to succumb to the
march of improvement; it will be replaced by another shed of
the type of that we have just noticed, but with a stone front
matching the exterior of the store in Rolle Street.   [This
improvement has since been carried out.]

Turning to the timber yard, let us give the public the
benefit of our new found erudition in things wooden.   Timber
cut in boards is "wood;" wood in baulk is "timber."   Of
late years the nature of the business has undergone a rever-
sion.   Messrs. Rawle and Gammon imported "timber" and
"deals" respectively, in proportion as ten is to one.   Messrs.
Rawle, Gammon and Baker have reversed these proportions;
for every ton of "timber" they purchase ten tons of "deals"
enter the yard.   We have only to take a bird's eye view of
the whole premises to corroborate the statement by our own
inspection.   Archangel and Swedish deals, built up in lofty
stacks, protected by temporary roofs, rise above the marsh,
which the firm are filling in for the purpose of excluding the
tidal water from the main portion of the yard.   It is their
intention to build a quay wall of a substantial character from
the Drawbridge to the boundary of their premises.   Among
the other contents of the yard, the tall ladder spars like so
many May-poles, and the English timber, with elm for coffin

board purposes, which is suggestive of thoughts lugubrious,
bring into juxtaposition again the ill-assorted associations of
May and December.

Now turn we to the Saw Mill upon which the firm have
concentrated their enterprise and industry. Not many years
ago all the work was done at the primitive " pit," and with
the fact before us that a whole saw mill, with modern
machinery for moulding, planing, grooving, and tongueing,
hand-sawing, &c., is now in full swing, we are invited to form
our own opinion of the advancement which has characterised
the concern in the hands of its present proprietors. Here is
the heart of the industry which most interests the visitor whose
profession has conferred upon him what the learned divine
stigmatised as an insatiable demand for novelty which is ever
and anon demanding, "Shew us some new thing." The loud
burr-r-r of the saw is our welcome, as, entering the mill, we
see a 44-inch " circular" reducing a length of timber to clean
cut boards. Idle for the moment, but speedily alert with life
and motion at a hint from our cicerone, is an upright frame
saw for cutting the better classes of wood. This is an
ingenious contrivance for working with upright saws, any
number of which are combined in the frame ; the cleaner and
finer descriptions of sawing are done with this admirable
specimen of mechanical ingenuity. A four-cutting, moulding,
grooving and tongueing machine ; an improved band saw,
cutting wood to any shape, with the greatest possible nicety ;
a guillotine, for cutting teeth of the saw at one sharp operation—are indicative of the thorough manner in which the
firm have adapted the means at hand in modern machinery to
their work. A 10-h.p. (nominal) engine, with 12-h.p. boiler,

F

gives the necessary power, driving the whole of the machinery
of the mill. The engine is of the inclined pattern, and by
using a boiler of extra power the firm are enabled to dispense
with the services of a stoker. A space twelve feet square
accommodates engine and boiler.

And here we may give our description a pause, to comment
upon the economical plan by which the whole undertaking is
marked. There is neither stint nor waste, but the works are
as compressed and compact as experience and good judgment
can make them. The firm have applied the principle enun-
ciated by " Uncle Ezek."—The most economical man is the
one who can spend the most money to advantage. The yard
and one or two buildings that " the oldest inhabitant " may
remember as the whole extent of the premises of the firm, have
been replaced by cottages, offices, stores, shed, and mill, and
when Messrs. Rawle, Gammon and Baker have carried out
their intentions to the full, the yard will be studded with
substantial sheds, completing the thorough improvement and
extension of the premises.

From the Mill, the English timber yard extends to the
boundary of the firm's area, contiguous to Mr. T. Horn's new
repository. The famous trio of familiar British trees—the
oak, the elm, and the ash—lie here, where many a monarch of our
woods has reposed after the woodman has dethroned him from
his lofty estate. On the other side of the raised path, which
is a by-way to Pilton, the firm are rapidly filling up the marsh
with "deads," and thus increasing the extent of their available
storage ground.

The business of Messrs. Rawle, Gammon and Baker is co-extensive with North Devon itself, and we may take it that the extraordinary impetus which the building trade of the district received in 1885, and which was maintained down to the present year, has had not a little to do with increasing that prosperity of the concern which has manifested itself in the remarkable way that we have indicated.

THE BRADIFORD TURNING MILL.

The little Bradiford stream which rises about two miles beyond the "half-way house" on the Ilfracombe road, and, after its short but sinuous course, empties itself into the Taw, which, in turn, is lost, as a drop in the bucket, in the Severn sea, turns half-a-dozen mills. Like the river of song, though men may come, and men may go, it still goes on for ever. Amongst other changes of which it has been a silent witness —nay, not a silent witness, for it sings a merry lay, this industrious little river—it has seen strange mutations at the Bradiford mill. Some sixty years ago, when George the Fourth was King, it was a "tucking-mill"—"tuckey-mill" in the vernacular—and the stream that, gaining strength with its journey and joining unto itself sundry tiny rivulets, went by here with a swirl and a slush, turned the uncouth wheel with the ugly hammers that beat the skin, for Bradiford mill was something of a fellmonger's factory in those days. Unto the leather-beating mill succeeded the wheel which assisted a Mr. Herson, of Litchdon Street, Barnstaple, in carrying on his little manufactory of rocking-horses and chairs. It was a very unpretentious business, but "old Herson's rocking-horses"

F 2

were not the least substantial articles in the market ; they were warranted to stand the wear and tear and the " racket " of the most mischievous of Barum boys—and that is, in itself, no slight testimonial. After the old stream had made merry over the making of rocking-horses—that was a manufacture into which it entered with all its life and soul—along came Messrs. Manley and Hayle, who saw the advantages of the situation for the brush-making business. The stream parted with the rocking-horses not without a sigh, but as readily lent itself to the new industry, to which it has adapted itself more and more as Time has laid his impress on the mill and the men who have worked it, and the surrounding scenes. Manley and Hayle became Manley and Son in the coaching days, and as coaching ways were not the best of high roads Bradiford mill sent out stout felloes and spokes for the coach wheels. The wood-turning in the time of Manley and Son was done by foot, and the work, though unpolished, was substantial of its sort. The foundation of what is one of the oldest if not the very progenitor of brush-head making businesses in the West of England was laid in the Manley *régime*. The younger partner had served his apprenticeship with " old Herson " of glorious " rocking-horse " memory, and was thus acquainted with all the advantages of the site on the banks of the Bradiford stream. The first circular saw found its way into North Devon in the heyday of this firm's prosperity, and when the business passed from the hands of Manley and Son into those of Mountjoy and Hancock, two respected and industrious workmen of the firm, the birthday of invention was celebrated, and the gradual introduction of machinery led to the continuous development of the industry. In 1869 it was that the present firm took over the concern, and the mill-stream, which was cognisant of the enterprise and go-aheadism of its new masters, prepared itself to witness great improvements. They were not long in coming. For the water-wheel with its wooden drum, an iron wheel with modern gearing was sub-stituted ; a self-acting iron lathe, for sewing mangel and paper-mill rollers, made its appearance ; the "little traveller," an "unpacked" circular saw, was joined by a bigger brother, "packed ; " a band saw gave new facilities for bent work which had formerly to be executed with a little upright "jigger ; " and a 2½-h.p. vertical engine gave place to a 6-h.p. portable engine for extra work, in summer, when orders come in thick, fast and furious. Of course this was not all the work of a moment. "Rome was not built in a day." Year by year the machinery of the mill has been improved, until we have a complete and compact little industry, which challenges comparison in the work which it turns out with many a more pretentious manufactory.

It was a proud day in the history of the firm of Manley and Son when one of the present proprietors of the mill was entrusted with two sacks of brush heads, with implicit in-structions to convey them on the hand-cart, which was the "goods van" of the firm, to Pridham and Hext's, carriers, in Joy Street, for transport by rail to Plymouth. Packages for Bristol were sent by ship at that time. Messrs. Mountjoy and Hancock now supply well-known brush manufacturers in Plymouth, Wells, Bristol, Exeter, and other brush-making centres, as well as far away Australia.

Planing and finishing was "hand labour" in 1869, now this, too, is done by machinery. The stove used for japanning purposes has doubled its size since the present firm came into possession, and this means the accomplishment of more than as much work again, for whereas under the old arrangement, 48 dozen of "handles" were "japanned" in a day, 120 dozen is now the alloted piece-work for the nine hours. There are seven lathes and benches, where nearly sixteen thousand brush and broom heads are literally "turned off" in a week, quite as satisfactorily as the "operation" was performed under the high standard set up by that connoisseur, "Hangman Dennis," the curious creation of Dickens.

There is scarce a household in which the bass and hair broom are not employed—at least, there is no English home "complete," as the advertisers say, without them. The hearth brush, the baluster brush, the stove brush, the lime-washer, the black-lead brush, the blacking brush—the whole numerous generation of brushes that the expectant bride catalogues when "house-furnishing" is her interesting occupation : these and a hundred other etceteras of the brushmaker's business pass through the first stage of their existence, as brushes or portions of brushes, in the Bradiford mill. Surely, there is not a housewife in the whole of the "West Countree" but what will be interested in learning how a brush is made. For, beside the more commonplace uses of the household article, have we forgotten the ultimate and excellent purpose for which the brush, with its differentiated ends, was obviously intended by its first manufacturer, who (correct us Messrs. Mountjoy and Hancock if we are in the wrong) was assuredly an "unprotected female"? If our memory has failed us, let us be reminded by the verse which accompanied the gift of a broom. Among the presents received by a newly-married pair was a new broom sent to the bride by a lady friend, the strange present being accompanied by this quatrain :

> This trifling gift accept from me,
> Its use I would commend :
> In sunshine use the brushy part,
> In storms, the other end.

With interest awakened by contemplation of these excellent uses of the broom head and handle, then, we shall watch with redoubled interest the operations by which the brush is made. Alder and birch poles are stacked in the timber yard of the firm, contiguous to the mill. They have been collected from the timber-growing districts of North Devon and the county generally, Totnes being no small contributor to the purchases of Messrs. Mountjoy and Hancock. The long poles are first cut the required lengths, and roughly prepared for the next process. They make their *début* in the mill at the "little traveller" circular saw, where their angles are toned down and the work of the turner facilitated.

The shapely little log, as it now appears, is passed on to the turner, who, with six tools and paint brushes, accomplishes the metamorphosis which turns the log into brush backs. First he takes off the uneven surface and turns the ends, polishing the now even exterior ; then he picks out the hollows, paints them red or whatever colour is required, cuts the little grooves which ornament the back, and with the finishing touch added, tosses them over his head to the heap which is growing under his industrious hands. The brush head, in this instance, has been turned in "double," that is to say, the little log we saw just now has been completely rounded, so that it remains to be split ere the back, with the flat hair end, is completed. The

packed circular saw parts the heads with great preciseness,
and at the boring lathe we see the hole drilled for the handle,
—this ingenious machine being a great advance upon the lever
arrangement formerly in use. It is a unique contrivance so
far as local manufactories are concerned, and enables 42 dozen
handle-holes to be bored in a hour. The hair side of the
broom head is now rounded at the edges with the improved
circular knife, and is then ready for the brush manufacturer,
who adds the hair or bass, as the case may be, and fits the
handle, when the broom is ready for Materfamilias and her
" terror "—the servant girl—to the garnishing of the hearth.
In the mill, it has passed through seven hands ; and four more
processes await it at the brush factory, so that eleven operations in all are necessary to the making of a brush. In the
course of a week one turner can manufacture twenty gross of
heads at the lathe. Of patterns of brush heads the name is
legion—each maker has his own ideas of the article which will
meet the public want and taste. In the pattern loft above
the machine-room we see an endless variety of shapes, sorts
and sizes among the manufactures of the firm.

The cunning of the hand has still reserved to it one
triumph not accredited to machinery, however, for the cutting
of the screw of the dainty pastry brush is still done by hand.
Among the curiosities of workmanship is the "ladies' toilet "
in brushes, picture dusters, furniture brushes, and the hat
brush, with their bent backs, as well as the spoke brush with
its invertebrate " spine," washing dolls, and last, but by no
means least, the round " back " of the machine sweeping
brush of the Barnstaple Town Council which, when repairs
were wanted, it was not necessary to go out of the town to

73

replace ; it was only required to pass the word to Bradiford mill, and Messrs. Mountjoy and Hancock were quite equal to the occasion.

And so, as our genial guide informs us, we might go on enumerating oddities of the manufactures of the mill without exhausting an almost endless series ; therefore we give this cataloguing up as beyond our scope and our intention, and follow him to the japanning department in the rear, where the hard bright black and the brilliant vermilion colours that make "things of beauty" of our carpet whisks and our hearth-brushes are applied to the heads and handles, in " coats," and dried in the ovens attached. The handle, or head, as the case may be, is given its first " coat " of " japan," then put in the oven to dry, next sand-papered by the .apprentices, after which its second " coat " is applied, it is dried once more, and comes out of the oven with a bright, polished surface, the " japan " as hard as the very wood itself.

There are other processes, such as the fine work of cutting oak veneerings, making the flat broom heads and the thin backs with which the bass ends are held, but enough has been said to indicate the interesting nature of the industry. The merry mill-stream has a part and a lot in the whole manu-facture, even turning the very grinding-stone with which the lathe-stools are sharpened. On Friday a freshet from the Exmoor hills gave it the depth of a mill-dam and the force of a torrent, and in its impetuous force it carried away one of the " half-a-hundred bridges " underneath which it flows " to join the brimming river." Years ago it would have swamped the fields adjoining, but Messrs. Mountjoy and Hancock, with the sawdust from the mill, have built up a substantial garden, and upon it—pay attention ye cottage gardeners—have laid out a well-tilled vegetable plot, the products of which will bear comparison with the growths in many a well-manured and professionally attended gentleman's garden! Sawdust producing giant broccoli! A hint to the wise gardener is sufficient! Bradiford mill, as may be judged from our brief notice, is an industry that it has been very profitable to become acquainted with. We shall value our brushes the more now we know how much ingenuity and skilled labour is employed in their manufacture.

VI.—MESSRS. VINCENT AND DUNCAN'S COLLAR FACTORY, BIDEFORD.

" Westward Ho !" has been the " sailing orders " of the collar making industry in the last quarter of a century. Twenty-eight years ago there was not a collar factory west of London. The world's mart monopolised this amongst its myriad manufactures. True, collars were made in Ireland and Scotland. To-day there is a marked distinction in the condition of things that obtains in this important branch of the trade in textile fabrics. Ilminster, historically associated with the manufacture of narrow cloths, was one of the first provincial centres of the industry. From that locality enterprising men have gone out, east, west, north, and south, to extend the ramifications of the manufacture, the demand which has grown with civilization and with fashion creating the supply in the proverbial order of commerce. There is nothing more striking in this growth and extension of the industry than the

persistency with which it has drifted westward. Leaving
economists to discuss the reason, we may accept the statement
as proven when we look at Taunton, which has become almost
the Somerset centre of the manufacture, and, following the
track of the iron horse, arrive at the "little white town on
the hill," which undoubtedly owes its present prosperity to
the remarkable accession which its industrial population has
received in the last decade, consequent upon the development
of the collar-making trade. Bideford now boasts of no less
than three collar factories within its own boundaries—an
offshoot existing at Appledore—and a thousand "hands" pour
out of its humbler homes on the six days in which it is given
them to labour, to "cut," to "stitch," to "starch," and to
"dress" those now indispensable articles of our English
attire—collars, cuffs, and fronts.

In extent, representative character, and completeness, the
Westcombe factory of Messrs. Vincent and Duncan, nestling,
as the name indicates, in the "west-combe" underneath the
new villa residences with which Bideford is extending its
borders Northamwards, justifies selection as a type of the
industries of North Devon. Sixteen years since Westcombe
flour mills were standing idle. Mr. G. W. Vincent, of
Ilminster, was in treaty with the proprietors with the intention of converting the mills into a collar factory. The
negotiations were carried to a satisfactory conclusion, and
with the decay of one industry the origin of another and far
more enterprising business was contemporaneous. The original
works consisted of what is now known as the old premises—
a single building of three stories and a tall stack. The block
that now abuts on the Westcombe road is the growth of the

last decade—extended, well-lighted, oblong, airy premises, built on approved factory principles, the engine room in the centre, and laundry, " stitching," " button-holing," " dressing," " stamping," store and finishing rooms, with the offices radiating from it. Three years after the establishment of the concern, Mr. Vincent took Mr. A. G. Duncan, of Manchester, into partnership. The more extensive structural alterations of the factory date from 1881, when the south wing was added. Improvements have gone on since that date, and, as the firm are imbued with that progressive spirit which keeps step with the forward march of the time, it is safe to prophesy that the works at Westcombe have not taken their final form as yet. Although, of necessity, collar-making largely employs " hand labour," the adaptation of machinery to various processes in the order of manufacture has characterised this, as well as most industries, in the inventive era through which we are passing, and our description of the way in which our collars, cuffs, and fronts are made will make it plain that Messrs. Vincent and Duncan have seized upon each economising " new departure," and availed themselves of the advantages which it confers upon producer, distributor and purchaser alike.

In 1878 the firm started a branch factory in a disused malt factory on the quay at Appledore, thus largely contributing to the prosperity of the little community perched on the hillside above the pool, where the waters of the Taw and the Torridge commingle after their devious wanderings through dear old Devon and efface themselves in the Severn Sea. A hundred and fifty hands are here employed by Messrs. Vincent and Duncan, and capitalists never bestowed a greater blessing upon labour than when the wives and daughters of those who go

77

down to the sea in ships from the Port by the Bar were added to the ranks of the bread-winners.

The cuff and the collar have but a scant literature, and we need, therefore, make but a short excursion into "ancient history" ere we turn to the description of their manufacture. Those who associate the overweening anxiety of the British race for the display of "linen" with the modern creation of the "dude" and the "masher" must, however, be prepared for the demolition of their pet theory.

> Time was, when clothing sumptuous or for use,
> Save their own painted skins, our sires had none,

sings Cowper in the *Task*, but civilisation and the collar, though not quite synonymous, were never far apart. "Clothed in purple and fine linen" may not have included the collar, but in the Book of Job we have the use of the term for that part of the dress, coat, shirt, &c., which encircles the neck. "By the great force of my disease is my garment changed; it bindeth me about as the *collar* of my coat," says the stricken man. But it is more particularly to the band of linen worn round the neck, of which the collar proper of our subject consists, that Macaulay makes an interesting reference early in that stupendous monument of his industry, the *History of England*. "But the name of the field of battle was peculiarly given to a new species of *collar*," he writes, this being one of the earliest intimations of the association of the band of linen with places and things which is now so characteristic of the article. The word, of course, is a legacy from the Latin language (*collare*—a band for the neck, a collar). In the English language the word has gone through that variety of

form which distinguishes every important member of the
writer's vocabulary.   "He smote hym with all his myght
through the *coler* of his hauberk," occurs in *Merlin* I., ii., 158.

The linen collar was obviously an afterthought, all the
collars we meet in early English costumes being gorgeous
articles, such as Chaucer alludes to in his *Knight's Tale:*
" *Collered* with gold, and torettes filed round."   " Good Queen
Bess "—as we were wont to call her before the critics discovered the haughty shrew beneath that regal deportment and
ample frill so fearfully and wonderfully made—should be the
patron saint of the starch makers, and the collar factors owe
it to the sovereign who set the fashion in the direction of
their wares that a redeeming grace shall be discovered in her
character.   " The Knights of the Collar " were a military order
in the Republic of Greece, and in heraldry the ornament for
the neck worn by the knights of any order receives this
appellation.   By the way, it may not be out of place for us
to call to mind the fact that both of the partners in the
Westacombe factory firm have worn the "collar " of the chief
magistrate in the town whose commercial standing they have
done so much to enhance.   Messrs. Vincent and Duncan have
" passed " the mayoral chair, and, though we can bear witness
that they are by no means out of collars, yet, in the civil sense,
—and this is no " slang," but a sound piece of English,
although a special phrase—they are "out of collar."   There
is a material distinction with a difference between the two
terms.

There is character in collars.   A man is known by the
collar he wears.   This may appear to be too sweeping a
generalisation, but one has only to give that prolific source of

caricature, the famous collar of Mr. Gladstone, a moment's imaginary contemplation, and compare it with the "band"— not of linen, alas !—worn by the typical young man about town, held up to wholesome ridicule in the music hall ditty, to be convinced of the grain of truth which it contains. Think of Eton and the wide "turn down" collar, whose generous "linen" reflects the presumptive wealth of the wearer ; the "Windsor," worn by the Constitutionalist, the "Hatfield" sported by the admirer of Salisbury, the "Rosebery" displayed by the partisans of the merry Earl : take a round dozen of different collars, and give a single thought to each of their distinctive descriptions, and you will see "what's in a name." Bobby Burns knew it, or he would never have written that piquant couplet in *The Twa Dogs :*

> His locked, lettered, braw bran *collar*
> Shewed him the gentleman and scholar.

But our reflections, historical, literary, social and moral, have been made at the expense of discourtesy to our guide who has been waiting to initiate the novices into the secrets of the collar-making trade. Let us console him for our dilatoriness by diligent attention to his explanations. The linen, which we may call the raw material of the collar-maker, is, for the most part, received from Ireland, and the calico from Manchester. The bales are stored in a room at the further end of the old factory, from whence linen and calico are given out to the dozen or so cutters employed in the cutting-room next it. The cutting is done by hand, with a knife very much like that of the leather-cutter, but with a trifle bigger blade. The linen is first cut to the necessary lengths and widths at the head of the cutter's room. Above the head of the work-

man who stands at his table, there runs a shelf on which are
arranged the numerous wood patterns of the various collar, cuff,
and front shapes. Selecting the pattern required, the cutter
fastens it down upon his layers of linen and runs his knife
around the edge of the pattern, on the raising of which we
detect the shape of the collar that is to be. Here the linen
backs and calico strips of the collar are also cut. We will
not stop just now to enter into details of the variety of work
done here, but follow our typical collar through the various
processes of its manufacture. From the cutting-room the
bands of linen are passed to the boys employed in the stamping
department. We have a "Reversible" under our eyes, and
the stamper selects his stamp, lays his little heap of linen
bands on his right, and the "clipper," which will receive them
after stamping, at his left hand. Then, with something of
legerdemain in that quickness of the hand which deceives the
eye, he brings over the pendant stamp upon each band as he
rapidly passes the little heap of about three dozen from his
right to his left, and "Reversible" is "writ large" upon
them.

From thence we follow the bands into the principal machine
room, a long, lofty apartment, where one hundred and fifty hands
are employed—a hundred and fifty, to adopt Wordsworth's
phrase, working like one. They are stitching together, with the
ordinary single and double stitch machines, the two, three or
four pieces of which the collar is composed, and shaping the
band to the form which it will finally take. To speak in
phraseology racy of the sewing circle, and understood of
needlewomen, the band is "run round," then turned by girls
who have "passed their standard" and stitched outside. The

calico slip is inserted inside ; the glossy surface and the back of the collar are of linen. With lissome, nimble fingers, and sharp scissors, the workwoman rounds the edges of the collar, making the place of the button hole appear, and, running the band over the edge of the table, ere she puts in the last row of stitching, increases the semblance of the collar. A hundred and fifty machines, driven by a central shaft, the motive power being supplied by a 9-h.p. (nominal) Otto gas engine, immediately below, may be set on their whirring way at once, the driving power being thrown on or off by a simple treadle movement.

"Button-holing" is the next "era" in the "history" of the collar. A special-make machine, ingeniously adapted to this delicate little operation, is here employed, some thirty or forty hands being engaged in this department. At the head of the room girls are employed in winding the cotton from the wheels to the "spools" of the machines. The inventive genius of the mechanician has cleverly arranged a mechanical contrivance for this apparently insignificant process. The button-holing machines are also driven by the gas engine below, a second shaft, carried into the packing department, where we shall pay our last visit of inspection, having been constructed for this purpose.

When the button holes have been fashioned—sewed round, but not cut—the collars are shot down into the laundry through a connecting shoot. Here they are washed by machinery of the newest and most improved type. This is the region of soapsuds and starch—all the miseries of "washing day" are protracted throughout the six days of the working week. From the cased "washer" in which revolving

G

chamber the linen gets effectually cleansed, the collars pass
into the circular "rinser"—a wringing machine of a novel
pattern that, by its rapid revolutions, brings the "day's
washing" within measureable distance of drying. In strict
observance of the well-regulated order of the laundrywoman's
operations, the collars are now starched. This is done most
effectually—by machinery still. Placed in barrel-like tubs,
with revolving centre-pieces that plough them in the thick,
starchy liquid, they are speedily saturated with the stiffening
pulp. Their next destination is the wringing machine, having
passed through which they are picked out by girls at the
laundry table, sorted, and tied in dozens, to be despatched to
the dressing-room. Washing, rinsing, starching, and wringing
machines—all are driven by the gas engine over the way,
which does its work with the maximum of ease at the
minimum of cost and noise.

The Dressing Department is another spacious room occupied by busy rows of workwomen, standing at long tables,
stretching the width of the apartment. Down the centre of
each table is carried the gas-pipe, from which there are
branchings opposite each workwoman, gutta percha tubes
carrying the supply to the jet in the gas-heated "ironing box"
with which they are 'getting up" the collars. Rapidly the
"box," with well-regulated heat, glides over the starched
surfaces of the dozen collars, giving to them that glossy
appearance which has so soothing an effect upon the feelings
of the respectable citizen. Smartly and swiftly the "box
irons" are plied, and the dozens disappear like magic before
the industrious hands and arms of the "ironers." At a
central stand are boys, who, with sharp knives, the blades

the exact size of the button-hole, deftly make the incision between the rows of stitching done by the button-holing machine aforesaid. One hundred and sixty hands are at work in the "dressing-room," each finishing the collars, cuffs and fronts after they come from the laundry.

Not all the ironing is done by hand in this way. In the laundry collars are being ironed by machinery with success which suggests the development of invention in this direction. The collars are laid on the travelling bed of the machine, which carries them to and fro under a bright-faced roller heated by gas; systematic, regulated ironing is thus admirably achieved.

Divided by a glass partition that admits of "dressers" and "finishers" seeing and admiring each other's work, is the finishing-room. Here collars, fronts, and cuffs are "studded and tied," then packed in the card-board boxes which, in turn, are removed to the packing-room, abutting on the Westcombe road, from whence, on an average, twice a day there are despatches of goods to the wholesale houses in London and Manchester, which are the principal purchasers of Messrs. Vincent and Duncan's manufactures.

As has been intimated, the linen collar is by no means the sole article made at the Westcombe factory. Coloured fronts of the numberless shapes, sorts and sizes that fickle fashion demands in her whimsical moods, and cuffs quite as endless and as charming in their variety, swell the number of patterns that we saw in the cutting-room. "Ladies' sets" is a special line and a popular one with the wholesale houses. It were difficult to tell whether cuff or collar has the advan-

G 2

84

tage in age and fashion, except that it may be the linen collar preceded the cuff of the same material, for the fold at the end of the sleeve of a coat or shirt is as old as—well, as coat and shirt themselves.

> Ripe are their ruffes, their *cuffes*, their beards, their gaite,

says Ben Jonson of the gallants, in *The New Cry*, Epigram 92 ; and the linen band worn loose over the wristband of a shirt is mentioned by Arbuthnot, who describes a subject of his sarcasm "in a morning gown band, *short cuffs*, and a peaked beard."

A final word illustrative of the compactness, economy, and independence of the factory, and we may turn the sandals of our wandering shoon in the direction of other industries. The card-boxes in which we have seen packed the "Reversible" collars whose manufacture we have watched are made on the premises. In one room we find stacks of card-board being reduced to bottoms and sides, and covers and ends, of boxes. The sheets are first chopped in varying sizes by the card-board cutter ; boys then "score" the boards where sides will be turned up from the bottoms of the boxes and ends turned down from the covers. The forewoman in the box-making department has a dozen hands under her eye, making the boxes by uniting the corners with glued strips of calico, and then papering the box, mostly with the favourite green. The glue is heated by gas, then laid in a thick paste on boards, upon which the calico strips and the paper are also laid in turn.

In the Engine Room we divine the secret of the motive power which drives all the machinery of the factory. One of Crossley's 9-h.p. Otto gas engines is employed, a 8-h.p.

Plate 9 (above) Part of Westcombe Collar Factory, Bideford; the building in the centre had once been a flour mill; 10 (below) many industries produced their own cardboard boxes. This illustration shows a workshop where coloured paper is being pasted onto cardboard prior to box making

Plate 11 (above) Appledore about 1885. Newquay yard is in the foreground with Middle yard, Richmond yard and Appledore quay in the background. The building with the bell tower on the end houses the present administrative block of Appledore Shipbuilders Ltd; *12 (below)* Appledore about 1890. The second building on the left housed Vincent & Duncan's Appledore collar factory

85

engine, of a different make, being held in reserve. By an ingenious arrangement, which conveys an idea of the economical system of the whole concern, the Otto engine has been made to serve a purpose which not even its makers have designed or suggested. In order to keep the cylinder of the engine cool by subduing the heat of the explosions which generate the propelling force, the cylinder is encased, and a constant supply of cold water plays round it. Under ordinary circumstances, this water, which becomes heated, is not made to serve any other purpose, but at the factory it is forced into the laundry and there used for washing purposes. Then, again, another judicious and skilful arrangement has prevented the exhaust gas from the engine, which would cause an objectionable smell, from becoming the nuisance it would be if not dealt with in some such manner. The blast is drawn away from the exhaust to an iron receiver, and by the time it has passed from this through a pipe to the outlet at the height of the roof of the factory it has been vapourised, and a nuisance is thus obviated. Mr. Colwill is the firm's engineer. The premises are admirably ventilated with two of Blackman's Air Propellers.

At the Appledore factory all work is done by hand, under the superintendence of two forewomen. The complete industry employs six hundred workpeople. With the bare mention of this fact, so eloquent in the picture it conjures up of homes supported, trade benefited, commerce extended, and the hundred advantages that flow from the partnership of capital and labour on equitable terms, we may well leave the claims of the Westcombe factory to be numbered among the primary industries of North Devon to speak for themselves.

VII—VAUGHAN'S GLOVE FACTORY, TORRINGTON.

In a list of such articles as might be imported from the
Low Countries, issued by the Imperial Parliament of Great
Britain in 1653, occurs a curious distinction between " gloves
superfluous " and " gloves necessarye."   For " superfluous "
read " dainty," and for " necessarye " substitute " substantial,"
and you have the difference between the glove we have already
described in this series of articles and that which is manufactured by Mr. William Vaughan, of Torrington.   The trade
in " fabric " gloves—gloves of thread and cloth, and delicate
lace and silk fabrics—lies wholly apart from the leather goods
business, the material and, to a lesser extent, the processes
of manufacture, being different.   The " fabric " glove is the
product of fashion, as the leather article was, in some measure,
the offspring of necessity.   In the sixteenth century, as we
have already hinted, the fabric glove was an imported luxury
—" superfluous " as our straightforward ancestors put it.
" Two piere of working gloves of silk, knit," from the Lady
Gray, the Lord John Gray's wife, were among the gifts to
Queen Mary on New Year's Day, 1536.   The body of one
of the early bishops was found clothed in a silk tunic and silk
stockings and gloves, the instance being known as the earliest
employment of this material in glove making.   "A pair of
gloves knytt of silk " became a frequent entry in ladies' lists
of articles of adornment in the seventeenth century, verifying
the maxim of Claudian,

> The people vary, too,
> Just as their princes do.

A fashion approved by royal princesses naturally commended itself to the commonalty, and, though we make no attempt to trace the genesis of the fabric glove, yet we may assume that when royalty smiled upon the dainty thing and was graciously pleased to accept and wear it, a place for it in the attire of English ladies was assured. How far it had progressed in popular favour in the seventeenth century may be gathered from a couplet contained in *Catch That Catch Can*, a collection of pedlar's songs published in 1652 :

> Come, pretty maydens, what is't you buy ?
> *Gloves made of thread*, and toys for your head.

But it may fairly be questioned whether summer's sunshine, the atmosphere of the ball-room, and the refined delight in light, airy, delicate garmenture, have not had as great a part in setting the fashion as the patronage of princesses.

We may at least be assured of the interest of the fairer sex in our description of the manufacture of the gossamer-like filmy material into gloves that shew off the shapely hand and the tapered fingers. Torrington has attained an enviable reputation in the glove trade for its special manufactures in silk, lace, and taffeta ; and in all the recent distinction earned by the local industry, the glove factory of Mr. William Vaughan has had an important share. Nowhere has mechanical invention been more largely applied to the manufacture, and few factories can boast of so many original additions to the make and fashion of gloves. In the height of the glove-making season the factory supplies to the market 24,000 pairs per week—just enough, we are reminded, to supply each resident in the metropolis of North Devon with two pairs a week. But we are anticipating matters. Let us first make our way to the factory itself.

88

" Vaughan's Glove Factory, in White's Lane, Torrington,"
are our directions, and, though " the native " affects a ques-
tioning surprise which merges into a slightly disdainful
bearing, as he informs us we have "just passed it," we
attempt a dignified rebuke of the smart young man who does
not perceive that we were on the look-out for a factory, and
not for an handsome building in an almost ecclesiastical style
of architecture.   There are factories *and* factories, it would
appear, but this imposing structure is certainly an exception,
in its external appearance and the internal arrangements, to
the run of " workshops " into which Her Majesty's Inspector
of Factories stealthily penetrates.

Mr. Vaughan is an hereditary glove-manufacturer, his
father, Mr. Thomas Vaughan, having carried on a flourishing
industry in New Street.   Succeeding to the concern, the
present proprietor, in 1884, migrated from New Street to the
building in White's Lane, in which he had caused admirable
accommodation to be provided for his employés, introduced
all the modern appliances of the fabric glove trade, and made
provision for the development of the business.   To Mr. W. C.
Medland, the present borough surveyor, belongs the credit
of designing a building skilfully adapted to the requirements
of the industry.   His plans were admirably carried out by
Messrs. Chapple (Northam), and Beer (Monkleigh).   On the
completion of the premises, it was observed that a splendid
addition had been made to the erection of the new and
spacious street.

The counting-house lies immediately inside the hall-like
entrance.   A wide corridor extends well-nigh the whole length
of the building, the woman's work-rooms, ending with the

ironing, tying-up, and boxing departments, opening on the right, while the long and lofty box making and packing departments stretch away on the left, culminating in the manager's room. Match-boarding has been used throughout the interior with marked success.

But our immediate business lies in the cutting-room on the second storey, and thither we are piloted to be confronted with the skilled operatives whose work it is to receive the raw material, fashion it into the shapes which taste and fancy and the inventive genius of the keen head that knows human nature and flatters its foibles may dictate. The cutters'-room is a well-lighted workshop, down the sides and at the ends of which are counters which serve as cutters' tables. On the right hand is a long row of lever punches or presses, into the use of which we are speedily initiated. For three parts of the length of the room the material department, a narrow corridor, very much after the fashion of "behind the counter" in an outfitter's shop, runs parallel with the cutting-room. In row after row of shelves neat packages containing cloth, silk and lace pieces, are stored. Here we handle a light package, and learn that the value of our parcel is £17. There, says our guide, is another, its contents worth £15. An opportunity for the remarkable mental calculator! The packages average in value £10 a piece. The store stretches so many yards, the shelves are several feet apart, and run to a certain height. Problem—What is the value of the stock-in-trade? Confessing our inaptness at "ready reckoning," we watch the material supplied to the cutters through the central aperture in the partition between the two departments. A ticket accompanies the "piece" and travels with it through its various muta-

tions. The Nottingham looms supply the greater portion of
the raw material, the nature of which has already been
referred to. The fabric is first reduced by the cutter to pieces
of the requisite length and width, according to the instructions issued with the material. The "tranks," as the pieces
are now called, are next passed to the puncher, whose operation with the press is, to the ordinary observer, one of the
easiest understood of the processes. The punch is a knife
cleverly shaped to the size and semblance of the human hand,
and varied as hands vary. Under it are placed three or four
pairs of tranks, and a gutta-percha block is laid beneath these,
the whole is slid underneath the press, and, with one swing of
the lever bar, the punching or slitting is complete. The
thumb-hole is pierced where the thumb should be, the thumb-
piece being cut by a separate knife in the same way. The
fact that taffeta is punched, much ,in the same way as the
leather, may occasion some surprise, but to the witness of the
process it is obvious that this ensures greater perfection in
the fit, and remedies the defect of narrow and short fingers
and thumbs, which would otherwise exist in these gloves.
But we are introduced to a genial glover, the sun of whose
manhood has not yet reached its zenith, who remembers when
the fabric glove was cut out singly with the hand. In his day
man has sought out many inventions. Now the delicate
Taffeta, the stouter Astrachan, the finely woven Milanese,
the filmy lace, and the soft silk are alike submitted to the
puncher, whose operation is carried out with a careful regard
for the nature of the material only second to the dexterity
with which he works his press. The "knives" are as
numerous as the freaks of fashion in gloves. The tiny

"punch" bespeaks a "baby's mitten," and this odd article
which has no fingers is meant for the manufacture of gloves
for Master Tom Mischief, who, if they gave him fingers would
soon bite them through—tiresome boy! This long shapely
instrument prophesies a pair of gloves for " my lady fair : "

> She reft my heart, and I a *glove* from her ;
> Let us see, then, if one be worth the other.

Progressing with the manufacture of the glove, we first mark
the destination of the thumb-piece. This is stitched round
the top by one of the girls, and then inserted in the opening
in the " trank " cut with the punch, by the glove makers
proper. The " fourchettes," or pieces at sides of fingers, are
also stitched in by machinists, the actual glove-making being
chiefly done at the homes of the hands in the town and
surrounding villages—Sheepwash prominent amongst them.
The parcels of unmade gloves are periodically issued to these
deft-fingered women and collected from them, the industry
supporting many of the cottage homes of England.

The first stage of glove-making, that of pointing, is, however, done upon the premises. A machine, the patent of
which was purchased of a German by Mr. Vaughan, who has
an exclusive right to its use, is now employed in this process
of ornamenting the backs of gloves. It works with two
needles, and has supplanted a contrivance which, though
ingenious, must have constituted the operation of pointing a
very tedious one. The work was held between two serrated
metal plates, which are cut with as many serrations to the
inch as are required for different sorts of work, the sewer
passing her needle through each serration, thus giving regu-

92

larity and evenness to the stitching.   Having placed the edges
to be sewn together between the pair of jaws, on an upright,
the holding edge of which was composed of fine saw teeth,
the sewer passed her needle back and forward between each
of the teeth, and in this way secured a neat uniform stitch.   The
" quarry pointing machine " of Mr. Vaughan's patent, so
successfully supplants the old style of round seam hand-sewing,
that whereas the average " turn out " under the old method
of pointing was, say three dozen a day, it is now twenty
dozen !   The machine works on the reverse side—another
advantage which it possesses over the disparaged hand-sewing.
But, even now, the old " quarry pointing last "—as we are
tempted to call it, so nearly does it resemble, in shape, the
shoemaker's " faithful spouse," is retained for finer hand work.
The examining room explains with its name the purpose for
which it exists.

The adaptation of machinery to the purposes of the glove-
maker is in evidence again when we arrive at the " topping "
room, that department of the factory in which the welting of
the wrist of the glove is done.   The machines are of Willcocks
and Gibbs's make, but they possess three distinct features
which specially adapt them for this process.   There is, in the
first place, automatic tension ; an unusually large driving
wheel next affords that rapidity which admits of the very fine
stitching done in " topping " the glove ; and, as a third
advantage, a new hand wheel reduces the " kicking " of the
machine—i.e., the jolting—to a minimum, promoting the
regularity of the work.

In the sorting room the gloves are received from the
hands and prepared for the " puffing " department, as it is

93

locally known—puffing being the local term for ironing. Orders are prepared here, and from the heaps of manufactured gloves, the requisite quantity is sorted, and issued to the finishing room.

There are few more elaborate finishing systems in the glove factories of the kingdom than that which Mr. Vaughan has introduced into the trade at Torrington. The " puffing " room might be deemed a facetious description, but for the fact that the " puff" with which the prudent housewife blows out her gloves is simply repeated with great elaboration. A row of silvered hands attached to so many upright iron arms attracts our attention by reason of its singularity. Underneath the counter from which these hands are thrust forth a steam supply pipe runs. From the central tube smaller tubes diverge, warming the hand with steam to its very finger tips. The steam, having passed through the tubes, condensing itself, passes between the hands and the tubes and goes out into the central shaft. The gloves are placed on the silvered hands and " puffed "—stretched and shaped. They are then passed back to the table in the finishing room, now tied up and banded, and are next boxed. We are now dealing with yet another independent industry. Mr. Vaughan is the manufacturer of his own boxes, and in this direction lies not the least interesting feature of the factory. But we must have done with the gloves first, ere we take up extraneous matters.

It was in the reign of Charles the Second that the short sleeves of the ladies' dresses brought in long gloves reaching to the elbows. With gussets of lace, embroidery at the back and on the wrists, and edged with puffings and pinkings, were

trimmed the gloves of those dandiacal days. The dress of the
nineteenth century has shewn a tendency to return to the
short sleeves of the seventeenth century, and at Torrington
factory we see how the glove with lace and what not takes
upon itself the graceful length of the gauntlet.   Gloves
fringed and laced make a very pretty show in the window of
the costumier, and not the least pretty, we ween, are those
manufactured at the fabric glove factory of Torrington. Queen
Anne may be dead, but the long gloves which preserved their
sway throughout her reign are still in vogue. With her, the
fabric glove-maker must toast the Empress Josephine, who
revived the fashion of long gloves. The Revolution, which
had no taste for fashion's follies, dealt unmercifully with
princes and the objects of their patronage, but evening dress
under the Second Empire saw these things of beauty again
worn. The popularity which the Taffeta and Milanese glove
have gained of late years has been sustained by the novelties
introduced into their manufacture. Mr. Vaughan has not
been the smallest contributor of the charms of variety which
have enhanced the prosperity of the trade. And variety is
not the only desideratum. Usefulness and resistance to wear
are also aimed at.

An entirely original idea of which he claims the parentage
is a means of obviating that wearing of the " tips " which is
characteristic of fabric gloves. This is done by sewing across
the reverse side of the tip parallel lines of chain-stitching,
which our guide, with an apt figure of speech, describes as a
" coat of mail " against the attack of the sharp nail which
rests on the rows of stitching, and does not come into contact
with the actual fabric. When the glove is finished, the effect

of this "patent durable tip" is rather to add to, than to detract from, the appearance of the glove. Mr. Vaughan has patented his invention, and the "Patent Durable Tipped Glove" is now one of the staple "lines" in the trade.

Another novel feature, which the firm has the credit of introducing into glove-making, is that in which the fabric, being woven a double thickness at the tips of the fingers, affords a special resistance to wear. The gloves which have this improvement are styled "Patent Doubly Woven Tips." The ornamented tips of the Taffeta gloves certainly enhance their attractiveness as an article of dress.

Primary, secondary, and tertiary colours have yielded up all their shades to the fabric glove-maker. There are one hundred and five standard shades, and these are duplicated, whilst there are eleven qualities in the gloves manufactured for dress purposes alone. Variety and beauty of material have their equal in the fineness of the work put into the glove. We may convey some idea of the excellence of the work of the glover's machinists, when we say that in one operation three rows of stitches are inserted within an eighth of an inch, neither row touching. It may have been this fineness of work that led to a peculiar stitch employed by a surgeon in sewing up a wound being styled a "glover's stitch."

The printing press has its rival in this self-supporting factory, for the "imprint" of the firm's patent is impressed upon the gloves in letters of gold. We console ourselves, however, with the thought that this is not the press that "rules the world," although its "publications" may encircle the wrist of women.

The box-making department is the centre of an industry
within an industry. Here diplomacy and dexterity meet, for
the box-maker has not only to be nimble with his tools, but
active with his brains. He feels the patriotic pulse of the
foreigner, and, as the manufactures of Mr. Vaughan enter
every European market, and find their way to the United
States, our Colonies, India, and elsewhere, it is his duty to
see that no national prejudice is neglected. The green-box for
the Englishman—is this suggestive?—stars and stripes for the
American, red for the Republican, and a gaudy mixture for
Brother Jonathan, a fancy box for the fair—in this politic
way the maker of boxes panders to our prejudices and (sly
dog that he is) says " You pay the piper, and I'll dance to
your tune." The card-board, stacked in huge heaps, is chopped
with an ugly guillotine-like instrument, and scored with
another less formidable, but more ingenious contrivance. Glue
heated by steam, aids the manufacture, and deftly and rapidly
the boxes are made and piled up. Neat pattern books, of
various sizes and types, are also manufactured.

The work-rooms of this building of handsome exterior and
interior are heated with horizontal steam stoves. Lofty, well-
ventilated, healthy, well-lighted apartments, they set the
Factory Acts at defiance, for the excellence of their accommodation is superior even to what the law demands. Mr.
Vaughan has cheerfully conceded that comfort to his employés
which he requires for himself, and which the magnificent
mansion now in course of erection for him in South Street
is intended to supply.

Machine hands, cutters, " punchers," " pointers," " toppers,"
boxers, box-makers, and outdoor hands—Mr. Vaughan em-

ploys some six or seven hundred in all, swelling the gains of the wage-earning class and heightening the prosperity and the happiness of the community in and about old " Chepintorington," for many a long day a centre of the glove trade. The products of this industrious host are packed in huge wooden cases, and forwarded by the London and South Western Railway to the London warehouse of Messrs. Ormes, Upsdale and Co., 4, Falcon Avenue, Falcon Street, London, E.C., from whence they are dispersed to the markets of the civilised world.

––––––––

VIII.—THE APPLEDORE SHIPBUILDING YARDS.

Appledore has a future before it. The reader receives the truism complacently, and remarks "Of course." But it requires no seer to discover grounds for anticipating the expansion of the " considerable seaport " at the mouths of the Taw and Torridge. What has been already admits of an increase of the present ship-building industry. In the lifetime of William Yeo, Esq., whose trustees still administer the dock property of Appledore, over two hundred men were employed in shipbuilding in the spacious dry dock and patent slip at the east end, and many a trim and taut craft,

> Ready to be
> The bride of the sea,

was launched from the yard, though ship repairing was then the principal occupation. The foundation of the industry was laid in 1853, by the late Mr. William Yeo, a large landowner in the locality. Mr. Yeo was the first to take practical

H

advantage of the splendid situation of Appledore—the first harbour and the easiest of access on the coast of North Devon. Beside the obvious geographical advantages of the seaport, there was the important consideration of the cheapness of labour in the locality. From 1853 up to the year of Mr. Yeo's decease the industry grew apace. With the departure of the guiding spirit of the enterprise the sun of the industry seemed also to have set, for, down to 1881, there was a diminution in the extent of work done and number of hands employed until the trade was almost threatened with extinction. This was in a measure due to the period of depression in the shipping market, when the English ship-building business was at its lowest ebb. With the revival of the trade, Appledore, which had sorely experienced the pinch of poverty, took heart of grace again, and from 1881 onward the prosperity of the industry has increased fast. The Churchfield-yard had been held from 1853 by the Cock family, who have been associated with the staple trade of the port ever since a branch of the Southmolton stock settled here. In 1881 Mr. John Westacott, a scion of the well-known Barnstaple ship-building firm, leased the New Quay Dock, and in 1882 Mr. Robert Cock became the tenant of Richmond Dock, under the trustees of the late Mr. Yeo. The history of the industry from this time forward is one consistent record of progress. What has been done suggests what it is possible to accomplish. The ship-repairing trade of Appledore is now limited only by the restricted accommodation. Hitherto the work has been confined to re-classing wooden vessels. Both of the firms which rule the roast are contemplating, and preparing for, the repair of iron ships which are fast replacing the "hearts of oak."

In the very eye of a sea-going traffic, by which is executed a very considerable portion of our carrying trade; with a harbour almost unrivalled in its facilities of shelter, and easily adaptable to the purposes of a dockyard—when the enterprise and the capital meet, and a breakwater is built, the extension of the docks of Appledore, the trebling of its trade, and the enrichment of its labour, must follow, as the night to day. Those who are familiar with the facts of the industry as it now exists at this port, who have studied its propinquity to the Welsh ports, and who know what competition there is among ship-owners to avail themselves of the advantages of repairing at Appledore, have the highest expectations of the future of her ship building trade. Once the loadstone of capital is applied to the enterprise which awaits its attractive metal, the prosperity and the growth of Appledore will be assured, and her primary industry will set sail, in a favourable wind, for the port of Success

> Like a stately ship
> Of Tarsus, bound for th' isles
> Of Javan or Gadire,
> With all her bravery on, and tackle trim,
> Sails filled, and streamers waving,
> Courted by all the winds that hold them play.

CHURCHFIELD AND RICHMOND DOCKS.

The Churchfield-yard and patent slip is the property of Mr. Robert Cock. The ship-building business has been in the Cock family since 1853, when Mr. William Cock, brother of the present proprietor, originated the concern. He was a victim of the cholera epidemic of 1854, and from that date

H 2

up to 1863 the yard was in the hands of Mr. James Cock, the father of the original proprietor. Mr. Robert Cock succeeded to the business in 1863. The Churchfield-yard and slip are at the west end of Appledore. Here, beside the offices of the firm, are blacksmith's shop, boat-builder's, sail-maker's and block-maker's lofts. Under the sail-loft are saw-pits, the circular-saw, with its manifold advantages, having been introduced into this department of the business.

In 1882 Mr. Cock acquired the Richmond Dry Dock, at the east end of the seaport, on a long lease. The length of the dock is 330 feet, breadth 42 feet, the depth of water on sill springtide being 17 feet. A hundred men are employed by Mr. Cock, and this number is increased at the height of the ship-repairing season. The men reside at Appledore, Northam and Bideford, each locality being benefited by the improvement of the prospects of the trade. English vessels, with stout timbers of spruce and oak, comprise the class of ships repaired in the Richmond Dock. The caisson has just admitted the *Isabelle*, of Swansea, 600 tons, owned by T. P. Richards and Co. On the foreshore being emptied of her ballast, is the *Kintore*, of Aberdeen, 1,700 tons, Messrs. G. Milne and Co., owners.

As we entered the Dock,

> Throughout the ship-yard's bounds
> Were heard the intermingled sounds
> Of axes and of mallets, plied
> With vigorous arms on every side—
> Plied so deftly and so well.

Left and right of the dock stretched storied stores. On the ground floor were saw-pits. Oakum-picking—an occupation

HE TORRIDGE VALE DAIRY.

SPECIALITIES—

REAL DEVONSHIRE CLOTTED CREAM.

AWARDED SIX PRIZE MEDALS, TWO CHAMPION CUPS AND NUMEROUS OTHER PRIZES AT THE LONDON, LIMERICK, AND BIRMINGHAM DAIRY SHOWS.

Established as Purveyors of Dairy Produce 1873.

H THICK AND A CREAM,

Packed in Derby and Old Barum Ware, to suit the Trade. :: :: :: (London Wholesale Agents : Messrs. CROWSON & SON, Smithfield).

Fresh Cream Butter.
New Laid Eggs and Poultry.
Choice Fruit and other Farm Produce.

PECIAL HERD OF DAIRY COWS kept at the Town Mills, and Torridge Vale Farms.

ddress—

3T. SANDFORD & SON,
Torridge Vale, Torrington,
Devon.

Plate 13 (above) An advertisement in the Torrington Guide 1895, showing the original Torridge Vale Dairy; *14 (below)* the dairy as it is today

Plate 15 (above) Part of
Chapple's Yard, Torrington,
about 1890. The tall building
on the left is still standing and
is now used as a builder's
store; *16 (left)* rolling hides,
an illustration of 1851

which has degrading associations, from which, however, it is happily free here—goes on amid the chat of old tars who, it may be, are eking out a pension by reducing the rope ends to thread-like fibres, used in caulking the vessels. Up the spacious stores—some 160ft. long and 24ft. wide—we mount, first to the trunnel loft, then to the mould loft, next to the several stores where paints and oils, skylights and companions, and ship's gear of all kinds await the needy vessel.

Descending again, we give the *Isabelle* an overhauling with what her seamen might style our "peepers." She has fifty men upon her, for she has to be re-classed and out of dock ere long, and the wholesome fear of "demurage" possesses master and men as the work goes merrily on. In the saw-pit odorous pine greets pleasantly our olfactory organs, and even nails and felt have an interest for us, as well as the rigging, rope and gear of all descriptions in this second store running parallel with the dock itself. With these illustrations of the many-sided character of the interesting and even romantic occupation of the building of a ship before us, we enter into the musically expressed thoughts of the poet :

> Ah ! what a wondrous thing it is
> To note how many wheels of toil
> One thought, one word, can set in motion.
> There's not a ship that sails the ocean
> But every climate, every soil,
> Must bring its tribute, great or small,
> And help to build the wooden wall.

Here is the pitch-house, suggestive of gruesome story. In five large furnaces the black, saturnine liquid is heated.

Barrels of coal tar are succeeded by minerals more advanced in " civilisation," as another series of stores invite inspection, sheet copper and bar iron being "the valuables" secreted in these strong chambers.

In the building yard adjoining the dry dock, the " pound " for the storage of timber occupies the foreshore, whilst yellow pine, pitch-pine, oak, elm, green-heart, teak and American elm—the felled giants of the grove—occupy the yard proper. By the saw-pits,

> Those lordly pines,
> Those grand majestic pines,

lie low and long.   Passing the board-making lofts, in which moulds are stored, and the timber yard strewn with " dead plank " seasoning, we reach the building yard, from whence the *Florrie*, ketch, designed for coasting purposes, was launched but a short time since.   Mr. Cock has purchased the yacht *Vacuna*, of Littlehampton, which, after a general overhauling, he intends adapting to coasting purposes.

Mr. Cock's premises cover some six acres, and when we have left the dry dock and building yard we have yet a block of stores to run through.   Across the road from the dock gates is a substantial run of lofts.   Rock salt is stored below, rigging above, and in the second storey sail-makers are at work with their " needle and cotton," whose size and shape would drive a seamstress crazy were she called upon to use them. Half of this sail-makers' loft is boarded off, Mr. Cock having kindly placed a portion of the room, free of charge, at the disposal of Church ladies, who hold a women's sewing-class here.

Beyond the felt and ship's gear store, where pumps, winches, and the thousand and one items of a vessel's outfit, are in waiting for exigencies, lies "the steamer"—where the planks are steamed and given the pliable quality which bends, not breaks, when they take that flowing line which has been termed the poetry of form. Then the smithy, where the swarthy smiths, stout sons of Vulcan, weld the metal to an endless variety of shapes and uses. There are four forges, drilling machines and iron stores. The glowing forge fires throw fantastic shadows on the walls, and we can imagine, as we take a parting glance at the weird scene, that we are assisting at the great ceremonial of the forging of the anchor in the brave days of old.

THE NEW QUAY DOCK.

"Maister, the barque's in the bay!" shouted the panting workman, as he ran up the aisle of Appledore Church, heedless of staring congregation and surprised clergyman, on a certain Sunday in November, 1881, to acquaint Mr. John Westacott, of the New Quay Dock, with the arrival of his "first job." Thereby hangs a tale. Mr. Westacott had resided in Barnstaple for thirty years, acting as the designer in his father's ship-building business, carried on at the Bridge Wharf there. In the days when the Barnstaple boating clubs had a West of England reputation, he had not only built the boats of the successful crews, but himself taken the "labouring oar." His sideboard in the dining-room of his pleasant residence at Appledore is still graced with the trophies of many "a stern chase" in boating days. In 1881 Mr. Westacott resolved to start business in the ship-building trade at Appledore. The venture appeared to most of his friends to be a forlorn hope.   For four months, during which no vessel reached the dock, their forebodings seemed to have been well-founded.   But from the day when the eager " tout " ran into Appledore Church with the " good news " of the first commission for the new proprietor of the Quay dock, there has been a " run of luck " which has pleasantly disappointed the lugubrious expectations of the self-constituted advisers of Mr. Westacott.

The New Quay Dock was also the property of Mr. W. Yeo, of Bideford.   That enterprising gentleman had built and repaired his own ships.   But, with his death and " bad times " for the shipping interest, the concern collapsed.   Three years prior to the advent of Mr. Westacott, Mr. Alfred Cook had been engaged in an attempt to resuscitate the industry, but without any marked success.   The fact that the yard and dock had been lying idle for years, while the trade had gradually drifted away from Appledore, was not conducive to the most sanguine expectations, it must be admitted.   But Mr. Westacott was made of the stern stuff out of which our captains of industry are fashioned.   To understand the disadvantages of the position it must also be remembered that the Richmond Dock was at a standstill, and the ship-building trade had virtually forsaken Appledore.

The first step taken by Mr. Westacott was the issuing of circulars to all and sundry in the shipping trade.   For a third of a year after this he was the waiter upon the tide of chances, preparing for the business which he anticipated, and which everybody else was convinced would never come.   The kick at the church door on that eventful Sunday settled the question.   " Maister, the barque's in the bay ! " was a fulfilment of the expectations of Mr. Westacott and a flout to the timidity of the dubious. The barque hailed from Bristol, and has been succeeded by a fleet of ships, British and foreign.

To-day Mr. Westacott employs just a hundred men. On special occasions he has had as many as 150 at work in the New Quay Dock—including one hundred and forty mechanics. He is contemplating the extension of the works and the introduction of the iron ship-repairing department, for which he has already made preparation. The dock is 270 feet in length, and 44 feet wide. Its draft of water on sill spring-tide is 17 feet. The foundation of the dock is at the present moment being sunk in order to give greater facilities. Lying under the shadow of the square tower that commemorates "Chanter's Folly," the dockyard covers an area of four acres, and possesses a foreshore of 400 yards. A gridiron 150 feet in length stretches along the New Quay. Mr. Westacott does not cease to protest that the revival of the industry at Apple-dore is in a great measure due to the considerate terms on which the trustees of the late Mr. Yeo let the docks in order that employment might be found for the hands reduced to privation by what appeared to be almost the blotting out of the ship-repairing business in the Estuary.

Writing of the distress which the lapse of the industry caused among the shipbuilders of North Devon, we are reminded of another serious difficulty which dogged the foot-steps of Mr. Westacott at the outset. After they had been waiting in vain for any appearance of the revival of the trade on the Taw and the Torridge, there was a general exodus of shipwrights from North Devon. Thus it was with the utmost trouble that Mr. Westacott succeeded in securing the services of eight men in 1881. But in the height of the summer's trade this year Mr. Westacott imported shipwrights from Plymouth and Falmouth, so incapable was local labour of coping with the demand, over a hundred men being employed at the height of the " rush " of work.

The repairing and reclassing of wooden ships, British and foreign, has been the chief feature of the industry hitherto. The development of the iron ship-repairing trade is to be a matter for the near future. " Ships are but boards," after all, as " sailors are but men," and to those who know the terrible strength of the sea, which has the power of a giant and oft tyrannically uses it as a giant, it is by no means surprising that, though they escape the fate of

> Ships, that sailed for sunny skies,
> And never came to shore,

the " life " of a vessel is a comparatively short one, and stands oft in need of " a new lease." Here is the *Lioness*, of Littlehampton, 900 tons burthen, in the East Indian trade, which has just passed the caisson, entered " the hospital " and submitted herself to thorough overhauling. The *Meridian*, of 200 tons, which appears to have had a rough time of it when the strong winds did blow during the gales of October, waits without. The *Carl*, 800 tons, has sailed after very extensive repairs, whilst the *Windermere* has been towed to Cardiff to load. Three other vessels are " on the ticket "—*i.e.*, their sailing orders are " For Appledore, to repair." These are indications of the remarkable manner in which the trade has improved of late years. For eight months past Mr. Westacott has employed a hundred hands, many of the men coming from Bideford and returning daily.

Among the new machinery which Mr. Westacott has recently introduced, there is a very ingenious contrivance for punching holes in sheet iron of various thicknesses. It is a Glasgow patent, called the Bear punching machine, and by the concentration of great pressure in a simple screw, it enables a hole to be cut by one man, through iron three-fourths of an inch thick, with the greatest ease, what was formerly the work of twenty minutes being thus accomplished in two. Punching, shearing and drilling machines from Glasgow, and from Sewerby Bridge, Yorkshire, greatly facilitate the work of the yard. The punching machine will make seven or eight holes in three-quarter inch plates. Plates of any size or thickness may be bored with the drilling machine. The punching and shearing is done by a combination machine.

The yard is entered by the blacksmiths' shop. There are three forges in the smithy. The bellows and anvils are silent, now, for the smiths are at their mid-day meal, which they take in a snug corner of the forge. Stretching away from the blacksmiths' shop are the lofty, spacious stores. Here oakum, paints, oils, there locus wood trunnels, then sheet copper and lead, next nails, and lastly iron—the hundred things that go to the building of a ship are one after another presented to our interested eye.

Out among the timber, in the dockyard, we hit upon splendid spars, 75 feet long—

> The tallest pine,
> Hewn on Norwegian hills, to be the mast
> Of some great ammiral.

Diving into the cabin of the *Lioness*, to find its captain

a most hospitable "tamer" of this wild daughter of the sea,
we emerge again to have a peep at the dock improvements in
progress, and take the bearings of the gridiron, provided for
the accommodation of vessels of 2,000 tons. On our right
are the carpenters' and joiners' shops, with the tool chests
of the workmen in the rear. Sail, moulding and rigging lofts
extend over the saw-pits, by the side of which lies a con-
demned spar—" a goodly apple rotten at the core." Then
the timber yard :

> Covering many a rood of ground,
> Lay the timber piled around ;
> Timber of chestnut, of elm, of oak,
> And scattered here and there with these,
> The gnarled and crooked cedar trees ;
> Brought from regions far away,
> From Pascagoula's sunny bay
> And the banks of the roaring Roanoke.

The lumber stores extend along the yard end, and the
rock salt which, pressed into the interstices of the woodwork,
preserves the timber and prevents the dry rot, is stored there.
Where the

> Columns of smoke upwreathing
> Rose from the bubbling, boiling, seething cauldron, that flowed
> And overflowed,
> With the black tar, heaped for the sheathing,

there the pitch was being prepared for the tawny sides of the
Lioness. The copper stores complete the round of the workshops and the yard, and we have just time to express good
wishes for the increase of the industry to the greater prosperity

of Appledore, ere we hie to the ferry, watching, as we glide
out of the port,

> The eddies and dimples of the tide
> Play round the bows of ships
> That steadily at anchor ride,

for Appledore had a brave show of craft on the day of our
visit.

IX.—THE DEVON ART POTTERY.

The history of the Art industry which has been developed
within the last decade by Messrs. Lauder and Smith, on the
marsh at Pottington, is one long record of a determined
struggle in the adaptation of the material to the artistic
purposes which the firm have kept in view with a determination and persistency which has now been rewarded by the
dawn of success. The annals of pottery—which are written
in clay, for the potter's art is prehistoric—are full of like
reminiscences. Bernard Palissy,

> Who breaks his tables and his chairs
> To feed his furnace fires, nor cares
> Who goes unfed if they are fed,
> Nor who may live if they are dead,

is a type of the potter, in his earnest endeavour to grasp
the secrets of his art and conquer Nature.

> This alchemist with hollow cheeks
> And sunken, searching eyes, who seeks,
> By mingled earths and ores, combined
> With potency of fire, to find
> Some new enamel hard and bright,
> His dream, his passion, his delight,

and who lives so realistically to our senses in the biography
of Morley, bore all the ills that potter flesh is heir to. And
here, in this nursling Barum industry, endowed with such
possibilities of expansion, defeat has paved the way to success
by inciting to renewed exertion. We have already, in this
series of articles, described the routine of pottery, and our
present purpose is to describe the development of a distinct
industry, paying especial attention to the details in which it
differs from that already noticed. It may be well to mention
at the outset that the method of manufacture and the nature
of the ware have no uniformity with the characteristics of
the beautiful productions of Mr. Brannam, at the Royal
Barum Ware Potteries, and that, therefore, as neither enters
into rivalry with the other, there is no question of competition
about which we need be concerned.

Twelve years ago—in October, 1876, to be precise—the
pottery at Pottington came into existence. Messrs. Lauder
and Smith had been made aware of the existence of a valuable
clay in a marsh owned by the Hon. Mark Rolle. They
accordingly acquired a lease of the property, and commenced
a series of experiments. Their first experiences were of a
most discouraging character, and in the hands of men possessing a lesser measure of that indomitable spirit which is our
national heritage, the pottery would have had an experimental
existence only. The concern had been worked at a loss for
a few years whilst the difficulties of the material were being
gradually overcome. In the birthday of the industry the firm
were content with common manufactures. But by-and-bye
bricks, tiles, and drain pipes gave way to ornamental ridge
creases, roof finials, &c. Then Art allied itself to labour,

modelling of a more ambitious character began, and the foundation of that horticultural department which is one of the staple features of the business was laid. The conservatory flower pot, various forms of " lawn buckets," tazzia vases, &c., were rapidly added to the manufactures of the firm. Ornamental orchid pots, in the form of pendant baskets, through the openings in which the orchids grew and trailed their branches, was a decided " hit," and is one of the most saleable productions in this department, the rich, red ware, with appropriate ornaments of oak leaves and fern fronds, being admirably adapted for this particular purpose. Encouraged by their previous successes, the firm now commenced the most ambitious and precarious development of the industry. The manufacture of art pottery was the next rung on the ladder which they determined to mount. In order to give some idea of the Sisyphean task which stood in the way of the accomplishment of their purpose, the fat nature of the clay, the inherent difficulty of firing colours in natural ware, and the discovery of the secrets of glazes and colours and their application to the peculiar nature of the raw material in use at Pottington, may be enumerated among the barriers to success that delayed the development of the industry in this direction. But difficulties were made to be overcome. The Devon Art Pottery is now on the high road to success as a business venture, whilst the artistic value of the manufactures is highly appraised.

Entering upon a more detailed description of the pottery itself, we note the very important fact that it is extending its borders—which circumstance speaks most eloquently on the subject of the prosperity of the industry. The modelling rooms, kilns and drying sheds were originally built upon the clay-fields in which the firm commenced their operations. Necessity has demanded an extension of the area, and, with the readily acceded consent of the Hon. Mark Rolle, Messrs. Lauder and Smith have leased the marsh on the other side of the Braunton road, where it is estimated that a supply exists sufficient to cope with the demand for the next half century. The area of the pottery, consequently, now covers five acres. From thirty to forty men are on the works, according to the season, the summer, of course, seeing an increase in the employment of labour.

Following the order of the operations in pottery, we meet the clay in its raw state, directly that it has come from the field. Messrs. Lauder and Smith's brick-making industry has steam for its motive power. The word "pottery," in its widest sense, includes all objects made of clay, moulded into form whilst in a moist plastic state, and then hardened by fire, so that we are quite within the limits of our subject in discussing this feature of the industry. Conveyed to the "pug," which reduces it to plasticity, in this instance the clay is "wiped" and lubricated by machinery, and the brick dressed and made by a continuous mechanical movement. This improved "pug" is the manufacture of Whitehead, of Bristol; the brick-press is by Clayton, of London; and there is a drain-pipe machine. The tables in connection with this steam patent machinery for the manufacture of bricks are the invention of the firm, and materially facilitate the work and improve the brick, disposing of the wiry edge, which disfigures the common brick. The engine-house adjoins, a four horse-power engine, by Roby, driving the whole of the machinery.

The kilns are three in number, besides which there is an oven. The brick-kiln is a down-draught oven. From the fire-bag the flames are drawn, over the arch of the oven down to a central flue, the fire never coming into actual contact with the pottery itself. The flue has a draught from the central stack, and by suction carries off the heat-fumes. The fire-holes by which the kilns are fed are at the side of the oven. The top of the kiln is used for drying the pottery out of the oven. In a second and smaller oven attached to the same stack, the fire is underneath and the flames play round the oven, not entering it. The other type of kiln in use is an arched up-draught structure. This is also employed in burning bricks. The flames come direct from the furnace on the floor, pass through the stack of bricks, the current passing out from the kiln through holes in the arched roofs.

Both the operations of making and burning bricks in vogue here are in striking contrast with those which appertained to the pottery of the fore-world, though the difference is less remarkable in the case of the kilns. In Isaiah, 41st chapter, and 25th verse, we have proof of the fact that in early times the clay was prepared by being kneaded by the hand or trampled by the feet. "And he shall come upon princes as upon mortar, *and as the potter treadeth the clay.*" The Egyptian kiln was a tall circular chamber of brick with a perforated floor near the bottom. In the Greek kiln there was a place for the fuel on one side and a door in the side of the upper chamber through which the pottery could be put in and withdrawn. The Corinthian kiln, except that it was domed over, was similar to the Egyptian. After expending large sums of money on various styles of ovens, Messrs. Lauder

I

and Smith have returned to burning their art ware in the ordinary kilns.

The bricks manufactured by the Pottington firm enjoy an excellent reputation among builders for the weight and solidity they lend to the structure. They have been largely employed in the building of other local industries—notably, the Bridge Wharf works of Messrs. Shapland and Petter, and the timber stores of Messrs. Rawle, Gammon and Baker. The pottery supplied all the bricks, plain and ornamental, for a church in the West End of London, built from the design of Mr. White, an architect of repute. This introduction to London builders might have led to the opening up of an extensive brick-making industry, but for the fact that the Railway Companies refused to meet the firm with any reduction of their prohibitory carriage rates.

Arriving at the modelling house we see the application of the deification of the art which prevailed among the Egyptians of the Ptolemaic period. With them the potter was a type of creation. The "potter's house," mentioned by Jeremiah, is indeed a place where thought leaps out to impress itself upon enduring material, for a well-baked piece of clay is the most durable of all manufactured substances. We have observed outside, in the extensive rows of shedding, how the fatness of the clay necessitates the exposure of the bricks on wood stands, formed of battens, sheltered under sheds, in order that slow and even drying may be secured. But no fault can be found with the clay on the ground of pliability. Consequently, we are not surprised to find some admirably modelled vases and pots, together with the endless etceteras of pottery which we will shortly catalogue in greater detail. Yet the amount of iron in the clay and its tendency to "pittiness" in firing have presented serious difficulties in the execution of delicate work. Architectural modelling has been one of the branches of the industry to which special attention has been paid. Numerous specimens of Messrs. Lauder and Smith's work may be found in the " ever faithful " city. At Buccleuch House, the new seat of Sir Whittaker Ellis, Bart., may be seen the coat of arms of the erstwhile Lord Mayor of London, and " Pan." The mention of Sir Whittaker's name also reminds us that the pair of splendid vases, 5ft. 6in. in height, symmetrically modelled and artistically designed, which were recently conspicuous objects in the show-room of the firm in High Street, now figure amongst the decorations of his splendid mansion. The manufacture of these vases was no mean triumph for the modeller in red clay, for notwithstanding their unusual size they were without a flaw or crack.

Local talent is entirely responsible for the productions of the Pottington pottery. And the watchword of the firm in all ornamental and decorative work has been " Follow Nature." In the vases, pots, and bas-reliefs of Messrs. Lauder and Smith we find

> The counterfeit and counterpart
> Of Nature reproduced in Art.

The modeller whom we visit at the stand supplies us with a ready illustration of the principle which guides him. By the side of the pot which he is "stippling" we notice a little bramble-bush, and turning to the pot again we discover its counterpart in the dainty border of foliage he has modelled

I 2

for the panel, which, in the finished piece of ware, will contain a figure.

From the modeller we pass to the designer, who, in this instance, is one of the principals of the firm. When the difficulties of the material had been overcome so far as to enable the firm to produce architectural terra cotta, in which some important work was executed for London, they sighed for fresh fields to conquer, with the result that they are now prosecuting the adaptation of the terra cotta to the manufacture of ceramic ware. The peculiar difficulties to be overcome in this direction were connected with the fixing of colours on the native red clay. By securing this object the production of an entirely new ware would be made possible. Our visit was most timely, inasmuch as it signalised the realisation of the consummation so devoutly wished. The fixity of the colour has been secured, and the development of the artistic side of the industry is now simply a question of time. "The golden lustre o'er the glaze," which is a characteristic of Majorcan ware, is the latest speciality after which the firm are striving; it is a very pleasing and novel effect—the cloud of gold dust on the red clay against the rich glaze. In the fictile fabric Mr. Lauder has wrought suggestions of ideal beauty in form and decoration which exact their meed of admiration. He has been mindful of the truth that

> He is the greatest artist, then,
> Whether of pencil or of pen,
> Who follows Nature.

Naturalistic ornament—figures, with which he interweaves his birds and fruit and flowers and leaves—in various styles of Renaissance and other phases of art, executed with the free, flowing grace of an unguided hand, is the chief type of decoration, and, it may be added, by far the best adopted by the firm. There is infinite variety in the shapes of the ware, from the dainty elicthysus and the greater Greek vase, to which the rich glaze and ruddy ware give warmth of colour that together constitute the finer specimens of the ware things of beauty. The smaller vases are decked

> With fadeless flowers,
> That never droop in winds or showers,
> And never wither on their stalks.

In the colouring of these flowers and the decoration of the ware generally the firm cherish the hope that they may create an industry in which ladies with artistic ability may be employed. So gratifying a solution of the problem "What to do with our girls," would, it is safe to conjecture, be highly popular with the "Society for the Employment of Women,' and the wider, though unchartered, association of mothers and daughters.

Included among the contents of the kilns, the opening of which was contemporary with our visit, were several successful specimens of the decorative ware in the manufacture of which the firm has now, to employ an expressive Americanism, "struck ile." Of the larger vases one was decorated with a cock and a fox—presumably, the victim and the victimiser—with appropriate foliage—and another with a flowing Renaissance design. In these, as in the choice examples of the ware on view at the show-rooms in High Street, colours of every tint and hue mingle in one consistent decorative design, the "scale" of colour on the red clay being particularly rich in its wealth of harmonious "notes." In the Sgraffiato ware the firm have attained their highest success, the graceful freehand drawing, the bold and natural treatment of form, with the cultured sense of colour and its appropriate use, bespeaking the true artist in the designer. The latest productions in the ware are undoubted works of art.

A brief concluding paragraph must be given to the contents of the stores, where innumerable tiles in bewildering variety lie drying on shelves, and rustic ornamental flower-pots, fountains red and glazed, umbrella stands, ventilating brackets, and decorated seed pans, stand out conspicuous amongst a host of manufactures. As for the architectural modelling of the firm, are not the bust of the poet Gay at the Grammar School, the dressings of the quadrangle at Tawstock Court and the chalêt lodge in the grounds, the shield with central domino and date on the Ilfracombe Arcade, and wreaths and coats of arms, here and there in public evidence, paying their own especial tributes to the successes achieved at the Devon Art Pottery?

X.—AGRICULTURAL INDUSTRIES.

In *Gulliver's Travels*, part II., Chapter vii, descriptive of the " Voyage to Brobdingnag," occurs this remarkable passage : " And he gave it for his opinion, that whoever could make two ears of corn, or two blades of grass, to grow upon a spot of ground where only one grew before, would deserve better of mankind and do more service to his country than the whole race of politicians put together." Jonathan Swift, who put this significant speech into the mouth of his literary puppet, was a satirist. Politicians became his bane. And in the bitterness of his soul he uttered this disparaging comparison. But he whom Sir Walter Scott quotes as saying, in a terrible spirit of prophecy, " I shall be like that tree, I shall die at the top," seldom spoke without consideration, scarcely ever uttered an absurdity. In this instance, laying aside the exaggeration of sarcasm, we detect the great perennial truth as the kernel within the shell. In a properly-constituted state, the man who increases the productiveness of the soil is undoubtedly a national benefactor. And, as assuredly,

> Ill fares the land, to hastening ills a prey,
> When wealth accumulates and men decay.

In dealing with industries the mutual object of which is to make agriculture a more profitable occupation, we are, therefore, considering manufactures about the usefulness of which there can be no question, whilst patriotism demands that their merits shall be enthusiastically appreciated, inasmuch as the national prosperity is enhanced by their beneficial influence. Bearing in mind the great extent to which North Devon is dependent upon agriculture, it is somewhat surprising to find so few manufactures directly associated with the cultivation of the land. Those which we shall notice are even now in their infancy, but their modest pretensions hide a possibility of increase and expansion which it would be idle to ignore in this series of articles.

" In a multitude of counsellors there is wisdom," but oft, it is to be feared, confusion. In the instance of the advice given to agriculturists of North Devon on the subject of dairy-farming, however, there is a uniformity which dairymen might with advantage reproduce in their butter. From scientists, from landlords, from faddists and from men of extensive practical experience we have received a consensus of opinion favourable to the provision of butter factories, as essentials in securing that important feature of uniformity in the quality of the butter which is so necessary to successful competition with the foreigner.   By-and-bye the North Devon agriculturist may be brought to see the advantages of co-operation in this direction, but at the present moment we are indebted to private enterprise for leading the van of the movement for the re-instatement of Devonshire butter and cream in popular favour and the extension of dairy-farming to the profit of the farmer. The Torridge Vale butter factory is one of these agricultural " signs. of the times," and from a brief review of the manufacture carried on by Messrs. Robert Sandford & Son we may gather an idea of the advantages of the new industry and its importance to agriculture.

Learned authorities also attribute something of the present depression in English farming prospects to the innate conservatism of the agricultural nature, which has refused to encourage that inventive faculty that has revolutionised other occupations by the application of new motive forces and the productions of mechanical genius to their several operations. Of late years, however, farmers have " come out of their shell," and the interest which they have manifested in mechanical improvements applied to agricultural implements has excited corresponding activity on the part of inventors.   The demand has created a supply.   The two unpretentious manufactories which we shall refer to in this connection have, of late, made some little noise in the local world, and, as indigenous industries, they are obviously entitled to a place in any work which purports to deal with the local labour-employing manufactures. This lesson was learnt long ago—" Never despise the day of small things." Here are instances in which the aphorism forcibly applies, for if there is any dependence to be placed upon the straws that show which way the wind blows, the " Star " Plough Works, at Southmolton, and Huxtable's Plough Works, Filleigh, are going to grow.

The Torridge Vale Butter Factory.

Ten minutes' walk from the Torrington Station of the London and South Western Railway, on the site of the Rolle Canal Company's Stores, is the pioneer butter factory of North Devon. Fifteen years ago Messrs. Robert Sandford & Co. commenced an industry the necessity for which is now recognised on all hands. Whilst others have been theorising the firm have been at work, and for years past the output of butter for the London, Northern and Midland markets, collected and made by Messrs. Sandford & Son, has run into thousands of pounds per month. The steam separator, into the use of which the agricultural societies are now initiating the progressive dairymaids and men, has long been at work in the Torridge Vale butter factory, enabling the firm to economise labour and to extract the cream from very large quantities of milk daily. We must visit the factory on a Tuesday if we are to see the interesting operations in full swing. The grounds surrounding the manufactory have undergone a pleasing metamorphosis since Messrs. Sandford & Son came into possession. What was a waste and a wilderness has become " a smiling place." Flower, fruit, and vegetable gardens environ the private residence and the manufactory which immediately adjoins it. The substantial original building has admirably lent itself to both purposes. The site is held on a lease of 60 years from the Rolle Estate, the Rolle road running through the property.

Making our coming co-temporary with that of the milk in the morning, we see the milk carts " backed " to the level of the top floor of the factory, the road being considerably higher than the front of the building. The rich milk—fresh from the cow, and unacquainted with the kine of the iron tail—is first weighed, then emptied into a large receptacle, with funnel-shaped mouth. This is provided with a strainer, through which the milk passes, to enter the receiving tank on the next floor, the capacity of which is placed at about 350 gallons. On this floor we also find a second tank, provided for skimmed milk, and a hot water cistern. Daily there is a washing of pans and a scrubbing of cans which ensures perfect cleanliness, the cistern supplying large quantities of hot water for the cleansing of the dairy utensils. The water is heated by steam from the 4-horse power engine which we shall by-and-bye come across, and which is the active cause of the whole mechanical working of the factory.

Returning to our milk, which we accompanied from the last to the first receiving tank, we now follow it on its passage to a smaller vessel. This is heated by steam, the milk being main-tained at a regular temperature. As it passes to the separator on the floor below we note the thickening effect of the height-ened temperature. Now we have arrived at the cream separator proper. It is a remarkable example of mechanical ingenuity. The patented separator in use at the Torridge Vale Factory has all the modern improvements. The fact that the fittings of the factory, throughout, were supplied and erected by

Messrs. Pond & Sons, of the Prize Dairy Works, Blandford,
gives a guarantee on this score. We present the mental calculator with " a little sum " in which he may exercise his peculiar
faculty. In the work of separating the cream from the milk
this machine is driven at a speed of 2,700 revolutions a minute,
200 gallons of milk being dealt with in an hour. How many
revolutions to a gallon ? Come, Mr. Calculator, speak up !

The separated cream is retained, either to be potted in the
pretty little jars, neatly labelled, in which Messrs. Sandford
and Son supply the rich luxury of Devonshire cream, or to be
converted into butter. The milk is thrown by the separator up
to the skim-milk tank we noticed in the room above, and from
thence pumped to the top-floor, where the vessels that brought
the new milk are refilled with the liquid, robbed of its richer
qualities by the cream separator. Thus raw milk is made into
skim milk while you wait, and a most interesting process it is.

The separator, together with a churn, a butter worker, and
a new machine for washing and re-making farmers' butter, is
driven by a 4-horse power steam engine of Blackstone and
Jeffery's patent. From far and near the farmers of the district
send their milk to the factory, receiving 7d. a gallon for the
cream taken from the milk, and utilising the returned skim
milk for pig feeding and calf rearing. Messrs. Sandford & Son
are not only thus creating what we hope is a profitable private
enterprise, but they are developing an important local industry
specially adapted to the peculiar requirements of the district.

The central situation of the factory, in relation to the
producing districts of the Torrington Union, is of great
advantage to the agriculturists who avail themselves of a
manufactory which, while saving them an enormous amount

of labour, gives them a profit upon their dairy farming which it is impossible for them, single-handed, to earn. To the fine old bridge spanning the Torridge near by, roads converge from the parishes of Shebbear, Black Torrington, Highampton, Bradworthy, Buckland Filleigh, Huish, Meeth, Langtree, Merton, Great Torrington, and many outlying farms. Then the Rolle road, kindly thrown open by the Hon. Mark Rolle, admits the farmers of Dolton, Beaford, Roborough, St. Giles-in-the-Wood, Frithelstock and Monkleigh to its facilities for ready access to the factory.

The co-operation of agriculturists in "running" butter factories, which has recently been advocated, is not a new idea. As a matter of fact, Messrs. Sandford and Son some-time since made a *bonâ fide* offer to the farmers of this district by which they might have become possessed of the factory on equitable terms. There was no response to the offer, however.

The factory is something more than a place for the manufacture of butter. It is essentially a dairy depôt. The extensive accommodation acquired by the firm and the amplitude of shedding room which they have provided in the factory and its surroundings, have enabled them to add poultry and eggs to their list of products from which they are prepared to supply customers in any part of the kingdom at a given moment.

The history of this innovation repeats the experiences of all pioneers of progressive practices. Messrs. Sandford and Son have a lively recollection of the "boycott" with which their earlier efforts were met on the part of the local con-sumer. The opposition was founded on a mistaken notion of the effect of the existence of the factory. Instead of raising prices, by stimulating and increasing production, its tendency is to reduce the cost of dairy produce. There is one fact associated with the influence of the factory on local trade which we must not omit to mention. The growth of the factory has been synonymous with the improvement of the monthly cattle markets at Torrington. The fact that this market is one of the best in the neighbourhood has become even more apparent since the inducements held out to farmers' wives to sell their butter in Torrington have been increased, and the commerce carried on with the factory firm has greatly developed. It is not an instance of drawing a bow at a venture, but rather a logical deduction, therefore, when the opinion is expressed that the growth of Messrs. Sandford and Son's interesting industry has contributed something to the improvement of trade at Torrington.

The " Star " Plough Works.

It is no secret that the successes which Mr. Bawden, the mechanical genius of the " Star " Plough Works at South-molton, has recently achieved in the ploughing-match field, have well-nigh ensured the speedy development of his little manufactory. Without entering into particulars, it may be said that there is a prospect of the great motive power of capital being applied to labour, with a future pleasant to contemplate for both. Mr. Bawden has confined his attention to ploughs, and many of his public successes have been won single-handed. He has given a literal interpretation to the excellent advice contained in the characteristically English saying, " Drive your own wheelbarrow." Mr. Bawden has demonstrated the advantages of his manufactures by putting his hand to his own plough.

We are not called upon to enter into a minute description of the smithy with its couple of forges; the plough platform which, in the words of the workmen, "gets things true;" the self-acting screw-cutting lathe; or the double-gear, self-feeding drill, with face plate and vice—an ingenious piece of machinery of French manufacture. What we wish to pay attention to in this case is the special features of the two ploughs which have been honourably associated, in our reports of ploughing matches and agricultural exhibitions, with the names of Bawden and the "Star" Plough Works. The farmer has been on the look-out for years for a combination implement,—a general purpose plough. Mr. Bawden's patent Turnwrest, or one way, Digging Plough, has been specially designed to -meet this demand. But this manufacturer has not neglected the ordinary turn-wrest plough; indeed, he is just engaged in perfecting this implement. Let us have a word with him on the subject of the new improvements which he is introducing. The ordinary turn-wrest plough—it may be remarked for the benefit of the uninitiated—is especially designed to produce the unbroken furrow, in other words, to do the crested work of ploughing. In the first place the new patent disposes of another of the wheels which carry the plough. At one time Bawden's was a four-wheel plough; he then reduced it to three; now he intends using two wheels only. Thus the unsightly wheels above the beam of the plough, the tendency of which was to overbalance it on hillside land, are disposed of, the land and furrow wheel arrangement not only adding to the appearance and utility of the implement, but lightening it and making it altogether much more acceptable to the ploughman and increasingly effective in his hands. The lever principle by which the transfer to right or left plough is carried out, is an ingenious, albeit simple, arrangement. The lever is drawn back, the wheels revolve together, the plough is turned over, and the wheels mechanically lock.

The ordinary long plough plate—to speak more technically, "the mould board"—is unmistakeably going out, and the short digging plate coming to the front. Seeing that the latter has the obvious advantage of being two feet less in length, and, therefore, much easier to manage, the preference is readily understood.

The newest improvements which Mr. Bawden has patented have, however, yet to be mentioned. His patent ring, abolishing the old "lifter" principle, is not the least important. This ring is a circular piece placed against the beam of the plough. The disc receives the body of the plough. There are two slots in the ring, and the body being held in these slots, the body and the share may be raised by means of the disc. In this way the plough may be adapted to the peculiarities of the land, as in the instance of wet, flat land, where the raising of the share towards the beam effects a saving to the extent of half-horse draught. The drawing in of the share, which, on moist soil, inflicts such hard work upon the horses, is thus obviated. Then, by slackening the bolts of the disc, it is possible to take off one body and work it as a single cut plough. The advantages of this arrangement need no description.

These are the specialities with the manufacture of which

Mr. Bawden is now engaged at the " Star " Plough Works, and it is gratifying to learn that orders are so pressing as to more than tax the resources of the little industry.

The Plough Works, Filleigh.

On the old road to Barnstaple, in Filleigh parish, where a stream, rising near the Devon County School at West Buckland, comes murmuring down the valley, Mr. John Huxtable, whose business, as an implement maker, was commenced at Brayford, in the parish of Highbray, has erected his new plough works. An oblong building, with the stream diverted to a mill-wheel in its rear, as we enter the glowing fires from three flaming forges extend to us a warm welcome. Mr. Huxtable has made his mark in the manufacture of ploughs, chain harrows, and expanding rakes. Upon these three branches of his work we will concentrate our attention.

But, ere we describe the manufactures in detail, we will have a glance round at some of the tools and the material. Here is a gauge block of Mr. Huxtable's own design. Cromwell said, on a memorable occasion, that " the man that hath a conscience in his work " was the individual who would win in war. It is yet more true of industrial, and mechanical, battles that where there is conscientious workmanship success follows. Well, this gauge block is a standard by which all the ploughs are manufactured ; so perfect a guarantee of the " trueness " of the implement is it, that every plough which has " passed " this " standard "—which has, indeed, been built by it, may be trusted to earn a good name for its maker.

In the manufacture of his implements Mr. Huxtable has had recourse to malleable iron—brittle cast iron made into malleable material by subjecting it to a regular heat in a furnace for a lengthened period. The ease with which this material is worked and its freedom from brittleness are important advantages, not only to the manufacturer, who thereby effects a saving of labour, but to the agriculturist, who is spared the cost and the bother of machinery of a brittle nature.

The motive power by which the machinery of the Plough works is driven, is, as we have already indicated, supplied by the purling stream. The water power drives an 18-feet wheel, erected by Garnish and Lemon, the well-known millwrights, of Pilton. The wheel has an iron frame, with wood "buckets." The main shaft is carried across the works and the different machines are attached by means of pulleys. A lever in the works, connected with the fender of the mill-pond by a wire-rope, turns on and off and regulates the flow of water, which is thus economised for emergencies. A rotary grindstone, in iron case, by Lee and Hunt, is connected with the first pulley. Next is a drilling machine from a well-known Halifax firm, made from the design of Mr. Huxtable, who has cleverly adapted it to his special purposes. The particular work in which it is employed is in drilling holes in the cross-pieces of Huxtable's expanding rake, which has more than a local reputation. The drill is of the multiple principle, admitting of three holes being simultaneously drilled in the cross-piece. Under the old system the drilling necessary to the manufacture of a rake would employ one man from a day to a day and a half; now a lad can superintend the drilling

K

with the result that in one day sufficient is done for six rakes, with far greater skill and accuracy than was possible under the old system. The drilling machine, by a simple arrangement, can be made self-acting ; its speed is regulated by a clever adaptation of the " change-speed " pulley principle.

The arm of the mill wheel lever is pulled and the self-acting lathe illustrates its purposes to us. Here again the mechanical ingenuity of Mr. Huxtable has been at work, the lathe being specially adapted for cutting the rack gear of the sliding-bars of the rakes. Two small circular saws, or milling cutters, of remarkably hard metal, connected with the mandrel of the lathe, cut grooves in the solid iron bars. A great saving of labour has here again been effected. Cutting the rack gear in the bars for a single rake used to employ one man for three days. With this skilful arrangement, one man can " turn off " in a single day enough for six rakes, thirty-six notches being cut on each bar.

The modern manufacture of the square link of the harrow is, by a simple tool of Mr. Huxtable's own design, now carried on at the rate of twenty to one under the system formerly in vogue.

From the machinery and material we turn to the manufactures themselves. And, firstly, of the ploughs. Mr. Huxtable claims to have considerably relieved the draught of the heavy double-furrow plough with his vertical head, and to have adapted it to use on every kind of land. In reversing the handles of the plough, a "gravity ball" mechanically turns the "hake" and gives more or less side draught to the plough, the draught chain having previously been adjusted to the class and condition of the land by means of the scale of holes provided for this purpose. Wet and dry weather and hard and soft ground can thus be "accommodated."

Then Mr. Huxtable has patented reversing appliances by which all his ploughs can be very easily and efficiently converted into diggers. His "digger" has this advantage—it pulverises the ground furrowed as the plough proceeds, just as the gardener, after he has turned the soil, digs it with his spade in order to separate the particles. The conversion of the ordinary plough into the digger is, by Mr. Huxtable's patent, reduced to the simplest of processes. All the ploughman has to do is to take out a bolt, remove the mould plate and the ordinary ploughshare, substituting a digging share on the same "shoe." The digger-plate is attached in the same way as the ordinary "mould board," and we have a digger plough complete. Here is an opportunity for the farmer to economise. Instead of purchasing a digger plough, he can convert his ordinary implement to this purpose. And here we may impart just enough of an interesting confidence to excite the curiosity of the agriculturist. Mr. Huxtable has, to employ language more expressive than polite, "something up his sleeve." The slicing of the soil as it is turned by the mould plate has employed the ingenuity of inventors for years past. Mr. Huxtable has directed his attention to the ploughing problem, and all we are permitted to say at this moment is that his solution appeared to us to be effective.

Then there is his patent coulter, which, to say the least, has been "a boon and a blessing to men" of the ilk labourer. The use of the old pattern wrought iron coulter necessitated that the ploughman should take it to the smithy every now and again to be "relaid." By attaching the stem

K 2

or shank of the coulter to the blade, Mr. Huxtable has obviated the splitting in the socket of the old pattern on hard land. The farmer can now keep on hand with each plough two or three blades (or wearing parts) and substitute them as the case demands. Attached by serrated connections, the teeth at the ends of blade and stem catching, the arrangement gives strength and facility of adjustment according to the nature of the land.

Another patent in which agriculturists have taken a very practical interest is that of the chain harrow. In the ordinary type of harrow, the chains run in one another's tracks, going over precisely the same ground. The object of Mr. Huxtable was so to arrange the harrow that the links should travel in different tracks, and thus produce more effect. This he claims to have accomplished with his patent harrow of screw bar links. One of the objections to the old harrow was the endless trouble caused by the hooks, or expansions of the harrow which prevented their collapsing, getting entangled. Mr. Huxtable has overcome this difficulty by placing a segmental or curved bar over one of the eyes preventing the loops or double eyes getting locked or tangled.

The final manufacture, which is a speciality of the Filleigh Plough Works, is the patent expanding rake, which admits of extension from seven to ten feet. The method of extension is by an arrangement of " lazy tongues " or cross-pieces, working on a pivot, with the opening and closing of which the rake is expanded and reduced. According to the class of work he has in hand, the farm labourer regulates the tooth of the rake. This is now done by the use of a winding handle. In the old pattern rake it was necessary for the farmer to extract every alternate tooth for the purposes of regulation. The rake, like every other patent of Mr. Huxtable's, is in great demand, and we may yet see it in the markets of the world with the other productions of these compact little works.

XI.—CHAPPLE'S YARD, TORRINGTON.

Nowhere else in the West of England shall we find an industry the like of that carried on at what is familiarly known as "The Yard," Torrington. So far as our North Devon manufactures are concerned it is unique. It was, therefore, included in the list of representative industries to be visited for the purpose of this series of articles as a matter of course. "Nathaniel Chapple, Chamois and Skiver Dresser, Torrington, Devon,"— whose business card we take the liberty of reproducing,—has the distinction of introducing a new labour-employing undertaking into the county. Forty years ago skiver-dressing was an unknown operation, west of Wiltshire, and the predecessors of Mr. N. Chapple are entitled to the credit of transplanting the chamois-dressing industry to the congenial soil of Torrington which still remains the single seat of the trade in the westernmost counties. Mr. Thomas Wills established the business on a small scale early in the nineteenth century. To him succeeded Mr. Westail, whose sudden death in a London street during the excitement of an election led to the concern being transferred to the Chapple family. Mr. John Chapple entered upon possession of "the yard" in 1843, and, after a term almost identical in length with the proprietorship of his predecessor, he too, with a singular coincidence, met his death in a sad and sudden manner. The year 1847 is still marked in local annals

by the 'bus accident on the Quay at Bideford which left a
heritage of sorrow to Torrington.   The Torrington 'bus occupied
its usual position beside the quay at Bideford, and Mr. John
Chapple, with other passengers, had entered the vehicle, which
was about to start on the homeward journey, when the horses
became restive and backed the vehicle over the quay wall.   The
tide was at its height and the passengers met a tragic death.

Mr. Nathaniel Chapple inherited " The Yard," and his
management of the industry was speedily characterised by
prudent enterprise which brought its invariable reward.   The
business, as we have hinted, had previously been confined to
the chamois-dressing.   But man had sought out many inventions since " The Yard " became the scene of a remunerative
manufacture, and fresh uses had been discovered for products
of the sheepskins which had previously been unsuspected or
ignored by the dressers.   The " skiver "—the part of the sheep-
skin now split—was formerly treated as refuse, worthless, except
for the purpose of making gum.   But Time, the great prestidi-
gitateur, has changed all this.   The rejected of the old-time
dresser has become the most valuable part of the skin.   What
a remarkable difference this metamorphosis has involved may
best be gathered from the material influence it has had on the
price of " pelts "—the raw hides.   Formerly fetching but 2s. 6d.
a dozen, they have reached as high a figure as 34s. per dozen.
At the present moment the depression in the trade has reduced
their value to about half the latter price.

The Yard itself has grown with the demands of the extended
business.   It has doubled its size within the last quarter of a
century—a change which has been reflected in the machinery of
the manufacture.   Some twenty-five years ago the traveller who

approached Torrington by the Bideford road would have had
his attention engaged by the curious operation then performed
at a "tucking-mill" near the aqueduct, where the chamois-
leather was then dressed. We shall see, in the course of our
survey of the yard, the advantages of the process which has
been substituted for the mill on the Torridge. But one substantial gain we can appreciate without further enlightenment.
The tucking-mill was two miles from the yard. Now the
dressing is done on the premises.

In the height of the dressing season seventy "hands"—
men and boys—are employed by Mr. Chapple. Trade is dull
just now, and forty employés are sufficient to cope with the
demand.

Beside the chamois and skiver dressing, the yard supplies
"pelts." In the mouths of old writers, pelt, in this connection,
was a familiar word. "Now here it seems the camel's hair is
taken by painters for the skin or *pelt* with the hair on it," wrote
Browne in his *Vulgar Errours*, Book V., Chapter XV. Even in
the classic *Virgil* of "divine Dryden" (Georgic iii., 672) it is
mentioned: "A scabby tetter on their *pelts* will stick." In its
strict dictionary sense a pelt is "a skin—a hide with the hair
or wool on it." The dresser purchases pelts from the fellmonger,
who has bought the skins by the quarter, from the butcher.
The fellmonger has "limed" them in the pits, then taken the
wool off, and in their wet, swollen state they are received at
the yard. Here they are fleshed and split for "grain" leather
next the wool, which is dressed (literally tanned) with a concoction of shumac, a peculiar floury stuff of the colour of sulphur
with a pungent Bohea-like odour, imported in bushel bags from
Sicily.

The skivers are pured with manure after they have come from the skin-splitting machines. From the " bate " they are transferred to the scudding machine—a row of brushes attached to a cylinder on which the skins are stretched. As the cylinder revolves the skins are forced against the brushes and in this way they are cleansed of the liquors through which they have passed. Before they are tanned they are submitted to a further process—a bran drench, the purpose of which is to kill the lime. The warm shumac liquor with which they are tanned admitting of the dyeing of the leather after it has passed from the dresser's hands, is contained in tanks, on the top of and entering which are paddles that beat the skins in the concoction until they are thoroughly saturated—in a word, actually tanned and converted into leather. The shumac gives a neutral hue to the skins, which facilitates dyeing in varied colours. From the tanks the skins are conveyed, by lifts, to the long range of lofts overhead, ascending which, storey by storey, we get charming bird's eye views of Torrington and its surroundings. A considerable portion of the lofts is of recent construction, the spacious, airy rooms having only been erected five years ago.

All the machinery, it may be remarked in parenthesis, is connected with the vertical steam engine of 6½-h.p., with a supplementary engine of 2½-h.p., which occupies a central position in the yard.

The various processes of splitting the skins comprise several delicate operations. Machinery has even in this instance superseded hand labour to a considerable extent. Here, in the splitting-house, is a double-splitted skin stretched on the cylinder of a rotary machine with an oscillating knife. When the skiver (next the wool) has been shaved off, the remaining portion, from which the chamois-leather (the lining, next the skin) is to be obtained, undergoes a second liming, ere it is fleshed. The "frizer" and the second splitter have a very delicate task in reducing the skins to an almost transparent thinness.

Although we are familiarised with the "skiver" in the form of book-bindings and the linings of deer-stalker and other hats, to the great number of our readers, chamois (shammy) leather is a more common article. Like many another manufacture, this chamois leather barely escapes the stringent clauses of the Trade Marks and Merchandise Act. General usage has, however, justified the description of "chamois" leather, applied to the hides of far less poetic animals than the graceful antelope of high mountain ranges. The skins of sheep, goats, deer, calves and the split hides of other animals are used in the manufacture of chamois leather, the inferior kinds of which we know as "wash-leather." In order to make the process of their manufacture clear we will retrace our steps for a moment. The skins have been limed, fleshed and frized in the ordinary way, and the lime has been again removed by mashing and drenching in bran. The skins are now subjected to a comparatively slight pressure in a hydraulic press to expel the water, then fulled (beaten) with wooden hammers in a tucking (or fulling) mill. This consists of an iron framework supporting the shanks of heavy iron hammers, which are raised by projecting cams on a tappet wheel. The hammers being raised to their height are released and drop by gravity on the skins which are contained in the iron troughs beneath. The end of the trough is curved, so that the skins are turned round and round by the action of the mallets. The skins are beaten by the hammers, which strike a blow equal to three or four hundredweight, for several hours, then spread, treated with cod oil, beaten in the mill again, partially dried by "staking" on the lines stretched from post to post on the green adjoining the mill-lane, or in the kilns near at hand, then rolled up and again fulled, this process being repeated for just twenty hours, that the oil may be distributed throughout the bundle. Taken out, unfolded, dried, re-oiled, and again rolled and beaten— these processes are repeated until the desired effect is fully accomplished. Heat is then applied to the skins through their suspension in the kiln, from whence they are taken and heaped in big open boxes, being transferred from one box to another in order to assist their thorough drying and to prevent combustion. The heat generated by the skins as they lie in these boxes is not the least remarkable phase of the manufacture, and we are not surprised to hear that when, by some oversight, a lot of skins were left untouched in the old tucking mill near the Aqueduct, for nearly a fortnight, they were discovered in ashes. The heap had not leapt into flame, but the skins had eaten their substance out, leaving nought but ashes.

The superfluous oil having been removed by a pressure of 250 tons in the hydraulic press and a short steeping in an alkaline lye, the skins are hung in the drying loft, and the final operation of "grounding" is carried on by workmen at their homes. Using a keen-edged, quoit-shaped instrument—"With a round beard like a glover's paring knife," as Shakespeare, the man of universal knowledge, has it—the parer, who has stretched the skin on a horizontal perch, shaves off the thicker parts still remaining, producing an even surface throughout. Suppled by stretching and polished by rolling, the chamois leather is now returned to the ware room. Here it is trimmed, again stretched to his full size, and laid out under weights, until the wrinkles have disappeared. Then the skins are sorted in heaps according to size and quality, and finally tied in "kips" of 2½ dozens for despatch to the wholesale houses. Glove manufacturers purchase the leather in the "crust" (that is, in the rough), treating and dyeing it according to the peculiarities of their own manufacture.

The truest economy is exercised by the skiver and chamois dresser. The parings of the undressed skin are utilised in making glue and gum, and the trimmings of the chamois leather are made up into the balls with which housemaids clean the windows. Materfamilias will perhaps attach greater value to her "shammy" when she learns the interesting processes through which it has passed during its progress from the sheep's back to the tradesman's shop. Chamois leather is largely used for surgical purposes, being extensively utilised in the manufacture of trusses alone.

Mr. Chapple's manufactures in glover's skins are chiefly purchased by London, Worcester, and Barnstaple houses. The chamois leather trade is, of course, co-extensive with the country itself. The productions of "The Yard" are shipped to Australia and occasionally find their way across "the herring pond."

If the Torrington dresser is in want of a trade motto he may go farther and fare worse than if he were to adopt the vigorous line in old Foote's *Mayor of Garratt:* "I would so swing and leather my lambkin." The Yard has played its part in enhancing the prosperity of the town on the Torridge during the last half century, and is destined to experience that revival in trade which has within recent date manifested itself in Torrington's staple industry—the manufacture of fabric gloves.

XII.—THE FREMINGTON POTTERY.

"Time's wheel runs back or stops : Potter and clay endure." And so, in this series of articles, we have again recurred to the industry which boasts the profoundest antiquity. At Fremington, in the quiet of modesty, may be found another son of Num, the directing spirit of the universe and oldest of created beings, who first exercised the potter's art, moulding the human race on the wheel ; he that modelled man out of dark Nilotic clay. To descend from mythology to more mundane things—Mr. Edwin B. Fishley, of Combrew, Fremington, is the representative of the three generations of potters whom Mr. Llewellyn Jewitt mentions as resident at Fremington. We may dispose of any question as to the qualification of the Fremington Pottery to rank among the industries of North Devon by pointing to the fact that the present Mr. Fishley was the first to solve the problem as to whether colour could be applied to local clay. He was a pioneer in local decorative ware. Mr. Fishley won the first bronze medal for ware at the Plymouth Art and Industrial Exhibition, 1881—a success which he capped by carrying off the silver trophy at the Newton Abbot Art Exhibition in 1882. He also received a certificate at Exeter.

Fremington can boast the most picturesque pottery, for the

premises upon which Mr. Fishley carries on his interesting
occupation abounds in quaint corners and curious " bits "
which the artist itches to transfer to his sketch-book, so
original are they. The ware shares in the unique character
of the scene, and it is nothing short of a delightful hour which
is passed in inspecting the holes and corners of the pottery
and picking up the odds and ends of the potter's art. Situate
on rising ground above the Pill and its pretty surroundings,
and with all the outward appearances of a country homestead—
an illusion which is promoted by the long range of low outhouses,
call of chanticleer and cackle of hens, strutting and pecking
about the open yard—the pottery is the centre of an old-world
picture of the life of the worker at the wheel remote from
towns.   It was established by George Fishley, grandfather
of the present proprietor, towards the close of the eighteenth
century, but the site of the original pottery was at Muddlebridge, on the Pill, some fifty yards river-wards.   At that
time, however, there existed a pottery at Combrew, and it was
with one of the employés of its owners that Mr. Fishley
commenced the manufacture of that Fremington ware the
soundness of which—at least, in Cornwall,—is a household
word.   Muddlebridge was probably the site of a pottery in
the days of long ago.   Evidence of the pre-existence of
potteries in the locality is not wanting.   Not many years
since, in the course of some excavations for building purposes,
tiles bearing a *fleur-de-lys* design and the initials " I W " were
unearthed ; they were worn, but were certainly locally manufactured and of Fremington clay.   Mr. George Fishley lived
to a grand old age, and, when " in the Nineties," passed the
hours that hung heavily upon his hands in forming curious

articles with the plastic ware. Jealously preserved to this day
are two very quaint watch-pockets which he modelled and
decorated with heads and odd scraps of ornament. A pitcher
thrown by him, and bearing, in all its richness, the golden
yellow glaze which is a characteristic of Fremington pottery,
is shewn with the name of the person for whom it was
intended inscribed upon it, together with one of the well-
wishing quatrains, the appearance of which upon the ewers,
jugs and loving-cups is a survival of an ancient custom. It
reads :

> Long may you live,
>   Happy may you be ;
> Blest with content,
>   And from misfortune free.

There are several other and happier instances in which the
potter, like Silas Wegg, has " dropped into poetry," which
will occur to us in the course of our description.

Mr. Edmund Fishley succeeded his father in the business.
His accidental death led to the concern passing into the hands
of the present manager, Mr. Edwin B. Fishley, who has carried
on the pottery for the last thirty years. Public attention was
first called to the Fremington ware when Mr. Fishley exhibited
some good specimens of it at the Barnstaple Show of the Bath
and West of England Agricultural Association. Here it
attracted the interest of Sir John Walrond, Sir Thos. Acland,
and " Squire Divett," of the firm of Buller and Divett, Bovey
Tracey. Sir John Walrond was so favourably impressed with
the qualities of the ware and manifested such an insight into
the possibilities of its development in the direction of decorative work, that he undertook to send Mr. Fishley some designs.

This he did, and among the specimens of decorated ware which Mr. Fishley exhibits is a fine copy of a Greek vase upon which is depicted the wedding of Bellerophon to the daughter of the Lysian monarch—decoration in white upon a red ground. The vase itself is not a copy of the Greek in shape, although an excellent example of the *amphora ;* and, beside the clever reproduction of the Attic decoration, Mr. Fishley has manifested no little taste and skill in the original supplementary ornamentation of the vase, consisting of a collar in keeping with the whole design. There were a pair of these vases, designed from the sketches supplied by Sir John Walrond, the other, which has become the possession of some lucky *virtuoso,* illustrating the classical story of Bellerophon destroying the monster called the Chimæra, the glorious god being mounted on the winged horse, Pegasus, received from Minerva. Thus encouraged, Mr. Fishley, who is a self-taught designer in the best sense of the term, turned his attention to Sgraffiato work ; with what success the bronze medal of 1881 and the silver award of 1882—each adjudged by eminently qualified judges— records. A loving cup, with a colour and an inscription redolent of " the rich Rhine wine," survives, with many another richly-glazed pot, as evidences of the taste and innate knowledge of the potter's art possessed by Mr. Fishley. One of the vases with figure and floriated design, the former of which was supplied by Mr. Ireland, an old master of the Barnstaple School of Art, marks another early stage in the history of decorative ware production at the Fremington Pottery.

From the first, as it appeared to us, the manufactures of Mr. Fishley excelled in one particular : their form was irreproachable. In the variety of shapes that met our eyes, as we ranged over the "throwing" house, the kiln and the store rooms, the symmetrical beauty of all the vessels was every where conspicuous, being as noticeable in the "penny joogs" as in the few specimens of decorative ware on view. Cylindrical vases and the common earthenware told the same tale. After all, there is much in the "throwing" of the vase. The pot is the thing—to adapt an historic phrase. Mr. Fishley himself throws the superior Fremington ware. "If you want a thing done well, do it yourself," says the axiom of our grand-fathers ; and this potter acts up to the spirit and the letter of the proverb. This truth he knows :

The potter's clay is in thy hands,—to mould it or to mar it at thy will,
Or idly to leave it in the sun, an uncouth lump to harden.

Mr. Fishley has some clever imitations of Japanese and Egyptian designs, and in numerous ways has shewn his *penchant* for the decorative side of his art. He has the material and the practical knowledge. There is, in a word, the nucleus of a most profitable art industry at Fremington, and the previous achievements of Mr. Fishley in this direction warrant us in expressing a confident opinion that were the alchemy of capital, skilled labour, and enterprise applied to Fremington pottery, it would bring into existence a decorative ware which would successfully compete with much that is in the market to-day.

But if the artistic department is as yet undeveloped, so much cannot be said, of the commoner sorts of Fremington pottery. Mr. Fishley's pots, pans, pipes and pitchers, his ovens and his "stains," are each and all marked by the superiority of their manufacture. Their shapes are good, their glazes rich and hard. Here and there a bit of moulding—a bead round a sea-kale pot or bread pan, and an ornamental trade mark of their own on the ovens—bespeak a liking for ornament on the part of the potter.

Here at Fremington we are again familiarised with " localisms "—descriptions of pottery which are a strange language to the uninitiated. Cornwall is a great market for the Fremington ware, partially, doubtless, from the facility of transport by water to which the Fishleys have had recourse in ' distributing their manufactures. Many a good ship-load of the big ovens in which the Cornishman bakes his bread, and pitchers and pans have left Fremington for the Cornish ports of Padstow, and Hayle, " Bude and Bos." The size of these ovens are calculated by " pecks." But a " 10 peck oven," in which " the giant Cormoran " slain by " Jack, the valiant Cornishman," might have " made his bread," is of far greater capacity than the " measure " indicates. These ovens are heated by furze burnt on the interior ; the ashes are removed when the oven is at white heat, and the bread put in. Another export peculiar to Cornwall is the fish " stain "—a pot in which pilchards are pickled. The different sizes are styled " great crocks," " buzzards " and " gallons." Fremington Pottery is sold by the " tale "—a way of counting which takes us back again to the banks of sacred Nile. Rustic flower-pots of appropriate design and well-hardened ware, and orchid baskets, the like of those which, at Castle Hill, contain, in such luxurious profusion, the flower beloved of Mr. Joseph Chamberlain, the " companion of gentlemen," are pretty examples of the manufactures.

L

Harvest jugs are a specialité of the Fremington pottery and one of its quaintest productions.   The rhyming injunctions to the harvester who indulges in " potations pottle deep " have tickled the fancies of many a connoisseur in pottery, and it is with little surprise that we learn of the sedate Lord Chief Justice having been inveigled into the purchase of a " tale " or two of these curious jugs by their originality.   Who could withstand such an appeal as this, for instance ?

> Fill us full of liquor sweet,
> For that is good where friends do meet :
> When friends do meet and liquor plenty,
> Fill me again when I be empty.

Lord Coleridge, at any rate, could not.   Then, again, there is this excellent toast :

> Success to the farmer,
>   The plough and the flail ;
> May the landlord ever flourish,
>   And the tenant never fail.

And the jovial huntsman, the shepherd, and the farmer will surely clink glasses with the men of the scythe and the sickle in pledging this " health " :

> Good luck to the hoof and the horn,
>   Good luck to the flock and the fleece ;
> Good luck to growers of corn :
>   May we always have plenty and peace.

These harvest jugs have a slip of pipe-clay on the red and are decorated, here with a leaf, there with a scroll.   But perhaps their manufacture is told to a more popular tune in another inscription :

From mother earth I took my birth,
  Then formed a jug by man ;
And now stands here filled with good cheer,
  Drink of me while you can.

The clay is obtained by Mr. Fishley from pits about half-a-mile from Combrew. By a judicious mixture, which is evidently a prized secret, a terra cotta of rich colour, a fine strong ware, is produced at Fremington. Mr. Fishley has also solved the problem of glazing the terra cotta bottle throughout the interior —a difficulty which potters generally get over by simply glazing the lip of the bottle, leaving the superficial observer to infer that the glaze covers the whole of the inside of the vessel.

Mr. Fishley has dabbled in tiles, and succeeded in firing a series which would make admirable flooring, the usual indications being strongly in favour of their wearing well. He has a mediæval design stamped upon them, the machine for pressing the pattern being of his own manufacture. This reminds us of another original mechanical aid with which we have not previously been made acquainted in the potteries already noticed. It is in the shape of a perpendicular pipe-making machine, which has certain obvious advantages. Drainpipes, of course, are among the most extensive manufactures of Mr. Fishley.

Among the quaint and unique vessels, whose shapes, peculiar and pretty, at once attract attention, are the " porringers " from whence our forefathers ate their nourishing "spoon-meat." Alas ! in the desuetude that has followed those "good old days " the porringer has suffered, and to-day we find it playing the ignominious part of paint-pot ! From porringer to paint pot—what a falling off was there.

L 2

Beloved of the colourist is the " yellow-drum " pitcher with
its rich golden glaze. In this instance, as in all others, the Fremington Pottery impresses the observer by the excellence of the
throwing, the goodness of the glaze, and the hard, resisting
qualities of this enamel. Through one ware room after another
pots and pans and pitchers are stored for the Spring market,
and anyone following in our footsteps a month hence will probably find these cleverly piled rows of vessels " conspicuous
by their absence. "

Although, as has been observed, the artistic side of the
industry at Fremington has, so to speak, been allowed to remain
in a dormant state, the ware is in demand for decorative
purposes. If not the rose, Mr. Fishley lives very near it.
He is now manufacturing great numbers of dainty little jugs
and large symmetrical pots which will be painted after they
have left the pottery. In the interest of industrial North
Devon we may desire the time when art and labour shall join
hands " on the premises " and another artistic manufacture be
added to those which have been reviewed in these articles.

XIII.—MODEL FARMING AT HIGHFORD,
HARTLAND.

In a district so largely affected by the condition of agriculture as North Devon is, no explanation is necessary of the
reasons which have led to the inclusion of a description of
intensive cultivation of the land among this series of articles
dealing with the Industries of North Devon. A suggestion
was made—not by the owner, but by an independent observer
—that the farm of Highford, in the parish of Hartland, and

Plate 17 (above) Throwing pots, as described in Section XII on Fremington Pottery. Note the labourer turning the large wheel to provide the power; an illustration of 1851; *18 (below)* a horse-powered pug mill. Crude mills of this type were used in most local potteries and brick works; an illustration of 1851

Plate 19 (above) The reservoir at Highford Farm, Hartland. The farm buildings can be seen in the background; *20 (below)* the harness room at Highford Farm. Note the terra cotta eagles

the property of Mr. James Berriman, " mine host " of the well-known New Inn, Clovelly, was well worthy the notice of the writer of the series, who had much pleasure in complying with the request, and was more than rewarded by the interest of the visit to Highford.

Early in 1878, Highford Farm, or the better part of it, was included in the expanse of moorland stretching away to the left of the traveller as he journeys above Clovelly, by Providence Chapel, on his way to Hartland. To-day, though Winter has laid his heavy hand upon the fields, the farm, far and near, is clothed with living green. Mr. Berriman has converted a wilderness into a smiling land of plenty. Bog and gorse, rushes and moor grass, have disappeared, and in their place are a hundred acres of permanent pasture, its emerald green glory rendered the more brilliant by contrast with the dreary moorland that bounds it on either side—just as a jewel gains in brilliance by its rough setting. We have to tell how this remarkable metamorphosis has been accomplished, and an interesting story it is.

Highford, let it be said, for the benefit of the reader to whom Hartland is a " far country," stands above picturesque Clovelly, the romantic village beloved of artist and tourist. From the higher fields of the farm a fine view of that delightful walk, The Wilderness, is commanded ; Gallantry Bower is visible ; sunlit sails on a summer sea may be seen ; and the rock scenery surrounded by majestic woods may be admired, where distance lends enchantment to the view. The valley intervenes between Highford and Clovelly, and the pretty homes of the fishermen, built in the sides of the almost perpendicular cliffs, are invisible from the farm, which is situated on the southern slope, retreating from the Severn Sea. The briny breezes mingle with the bracing ozone of the moorland, and that the few isolated inhabitants do not want for fresh air may be gathered from the fact that Highford is 550 feet above the level of the sea.

If we are to appreciate the force of the experiments carried on in this attempt at model farming, we must first take stock of the originator and supporter of the whole matter. Mr. James Berriman is not only the architect of his own farm buildings but is the architect of his fortune. His grandfather built a modest fisherman's cottage with stones carried on his own broad back from Clovelly pier to the cliff side. The father of the farmer of Highford was a " native," and his son has spent but few of his days out of Clovelly. He has been a sailor, innkeeper, lime-burner, and farmer by turns, and with the remarkable " knack " which the tar possesses, appears to be a Jack-of-all-trades—and, what is exceptional, a master of all. His uniform success is the criterion.

Mr. Berriman, like famous Hugh Miller, the geologist, gives a left-handed compliment to his schoolmaster. His schooling appears to have consisted chiefly of frequent and liberal applications of a *lignum vitæ* ruler. Mr. Berriman does not look upon this as an unmixed evil. As he facetiously puts it, the " soft heads " went under in this curriculum, and the " hard heads " came through the ordeal, becoming monuments of the wisdom of that winnowing principle—the survival of the fittest.

Mr. Berriman, in a word, is a product—and a remarkable product—of insularity. He is a strong type of local character

—that local character which, as someone has aptly said, the
iron horse ran over and killed. Isolated localities like little
Clovelly produce individuals built on plans and specifications
of their own, without regard to the prejudices and convention-
alities of the outside world. They are born in the town, live
to a good old age in the town, and never go out of the town
until they are finally laid under it. The entire world of the
inhabitants is incorporated within a score square miles. To
many a Clovellian to-day, Barnstaple is hazy, Exeter a name,
and London an unknown quantity. Mr. Berriman has, to
quote brother Jonathan, " made his pile," and now, in

> An old age, serene and bright,
> And lovely as a Lapland night,

he has means and leisure to cultivate his hobbies. He is a
profound believer in the great possibilities of cultivation, and
he is putting his ideas into practice. This brings us back from
a slight, but not unnecessary, digression to the farm itself.

Mr. Berriman purchased the property, which consists of
111 acres, from Mr. John Heard, of Plymouth. The condition
of the land then was very similar to that of the fields in the
immediate vicinity at the present day, where gorse and moor
grass run riot. Previous to 1878 Mr. Berriman had been
building up a huge manure heap. For years it was growing,
and people grew curious about " that dunghill of Mr. Berriman's." From far and near he collected manure and bided his
time. " Berriman's Folly " was the local word for the curious
structure, but at least the wonderers may have admitted that
there was method in the madness. In 1878 they learnt a
lesson. First, the gorse and the moor grass had notice to quit

from Highford, and the land was cleared. The fields were generously dressed with natural and artificial manures, and drained. The first year's crop was corn. Root crops succeeded. Then Mr. Berryman developed his idea of laying down the whole acreage in permanent pasture. The growth of natural grass was encouraged, and grass seeds were sown. The land, which would have been highly valued at 3s. to 5s. per acre, advanced in worth, until now he would be a lucky purchaser who found Mr. Berriman disposed to part with it at £2 per acre. "Ah," said the wiseacres, when the gorse was being removed and the moor grass exterminated, "'twill grow up again, Mr. Berriman ; mark our words, 'twill grow again." Mr. Berriman believed otherwise, and his confidence has been justified. There is a weed which grows in the Hartland district for which the local name is " Devil's beard "—a farmer's tormentor upon which he has revenged himself by giving it "a bad name." " Does any devil's beard grow upon your land, Mr. Berriman ? " said a labourer on an off farm, some little time ago. " Devil's beard ! my dear fellow," jocularly replied Mr. Berriman, " I don't allow him even to shave there ! " To all intents and purposes, the land has, indeed, been thoroughly reclaimed. But this, of course, has been the work of years. Rome was not built in a day. Between the uncultivated, undrained moorland and the dilapidated buildings of 1878 and a permanent pasture farm there was a great gulf. Mr. Berriman has bridged it. And this is how he went to work.

One half of the land was bog and furze. The bog was utilised for water. A quarry was found "near home," and Mr. Berriman commenced to build. The tumble-down outhouses were to be replaced by farm buildings of modern design and with every convenience. Mr. Berriman was a novice in farming. This did not deter him from preparing his plans and getting out his own quantities. But the drainage of the fields was the first necessity, and their owner took upon himself the rôle of an engineer. He saw that from the bog in the field next the Hartland Road there was a natural fall northward to the extent of the property. His eminently practical mind seized upon this fact, and made it the basis of his drainage scheme. He laid 4,000 feet of lead pipe from the bog through the fields to fountains conveniently placed in each, for the cattle to slake their thirst, and to the farmhouse and buildings. The property thus became self supplied with water. When we come to describe the farm, as it is at present, we shall see how admirable is the arrangement of the water supply.

The dilapidated condition of the farm-house and out-buildings called aloud on Mr. Berriman to rise and build. He was disposed to carry out extensive alterations, but an essential to the undertaking was the discovery of a quarry near at hand from which the stone might be drawn. He is a practical geologist, and a walk by the streamlet in the valley laid bare the strata of the district to his discerning eyes. Reasoning from generalities to particulars, he hit upon a spot scarce fifty yards from the farm itself, and set the quarrymen at work. "There's no stone there !" said the incredulous. "Dig," was Mr. Berriman's sententious reply. "I pay you for your labour whether there's stone there or not." They dug and they found a fine quarry, which is not only being drawn upon for supplies of stone to this day, but will be available for a long term here-after. But one difficulty presented itself ; there was a rush of water. Mr. Berriman was ready for the emergency. He caused a subterranean passage to be constructed, by which the water was conveyed away. Stone was now obtainable in abundance, where its existence had been unsuspected.

Mr. Berriman then razed the old buildings to the ground and commenced to rebuild. Like the boy boatbuilder, he has built them " all out of his own head." The man who built a vessel of an original type with sails of a novel fashion, that the sailmakers quizzed over, but which caused the boat to spank along like a racing sea-horse, has not found any difficulty in planning farm-buildings of a most approved and convenient type. He began to build, we have said. Yes, and this was the " staff" he then commanded—a veteran pony, of thirty years' acquaintance with the office of beast of burden, and, as Mr. Berriman puts it, " two masons and a piece." The " piece " in question is a mason with one arm, who, however, is an excellent workman, notwithstanding his irreparable loss. Tommy, the pony, who drew the stones for the earlier buildings, is now superannuated ; he has drawn his last load, and after over thirty years' labour, lives in clover, guiltless of the currycomb.

If we now turn to a description of the farm as it presents itself to the eye of the visitor to-day, the progress of the work of reclamation will be observed on every hand. The homestead first attracts attention. The farmhouse itself has yet to come under the hand of the renovator, but the out-buildings are new and of a model character. A pillared-gate admits to the out-buildings, which form three sides of a square. A wall of solid masonry bounds the yard on the right, and enclosed within a second wall there is a fine vegetable garden, to which access is gained through another massive pillared gate. A fountain plays in the centre of the farmyard, the water being self-supplied from the reservoir which has replaced the bog in the fields above. The buildings consist of cattle sheds, barn, granary, carriage house, harness room, dairy and stables—the three latter being in course of construction. The erections are of local stone, slate and wood. They are buttressed and faced with brick, the roofs crowned with ornamental creasing, and the gable ends finished with a miniature spire. An imitation of a string course in white brick relieves the buttresses. The rain water-pipes are, for the most part, carried through the buttresses, except where they are partially placed in grooves, the idea throughout being to have no obstruction which the cattle can injure. The style of the buildings is tasteful, and, while the practical has been firmly kept in view, the ornamental has not been entirely ignored.

The first range of buildings, on the left of the entrance, consists of a spacious carriage house, a cart house which will eventually be utilised for machinery, the dairy which will stand next, then the harness room, and finally the stables. The stables will extend forty feet, and will accommodate six horses, there being two loose boxes and four stalls ; the dairy will be 14ft. by 23ft., and the harness room will have a 11ft. frontage. The second range of buildings consists of cattle shedding for fattening purposes, on the ground floor, with granary above, and open stock shedding. Every space is utilised, a w.c. and lavatory being placed under the steps at one end of the central building and a tool house at the other. The cattle sheds are laid out on an original plan. Each beast has its crib, but the water trough in the centre of the stall which accommodates

two, is accessible to the both, though neither ox can trespass
upon his stall-fellow's crib.   There is a rack above the head of
the cattle for fodder, and an opening over each crib on to the
path at the rear of the stalls, from which the oxen are fed with
roots, a central door at the back opening on to the mowhay,
whence supplies of fodder and roots are conveyed to the sheds.
The water supply is from the reservoir on the site of the bog,
each stall being self-supplying.   At one end there is a connection for a hose with which the stalls and the whole run of
shedding may be washed down.   There is a gate to every stall,
and, in this instance, as in that of the doors by which the
shedding is entered, gate and door fall into their places automatically, and are, therefore, out of the way of man and beast,
the passage being kept clear.   In every door and window
provision is made for ventilation.   Eighteen head of cattle
(two in a stall) can be accommodated in this wholesome,
comfortable run of shedding, the entire length of which is
eighty feet.   Through trap-hatches in the roof grain foods are
supplied.   Outside the shed there are steps leading to the
stores, whence fodder and corn are conveyed.   The mowhay
will eventually stand directly at the back of these sheds,
which, by the way, will be solely used for dairy or fattening
purposes.   A wall will stand between the mowhay and the
meadow, protecting the former from the cattle.   On the right
of the entrance, and running at right angles to the sheds
already described, is seventy-four feet of shedding for young
steers; a central wall divides the whole building, which has
gable ends, is lighted with glass windows, and is well ventilated
throughout.

   Passing up the front flight of steps from the cattle sheds

to the granary, the provision of another little convenience
witnesses to the eye for detail which Mr. Berriman possesses.
In the outer wall of the steps a scraper has been inserted.   At
the top of the flight, a bird's eye view of the northern side
of the farm is gained, every inch of the land being clearly
outlined by its greenness, in pleasant contrast with the parched,
arid appearance of other land bordering upon it. Mr. Berriman
is the uncompromising foe of rodents.   Rats and mice are a
pet abomination, and when they enter the premises must
surreptitiously approach it in miller's bags or corn merchant's
sacks.   For the doors of the granary are covered and lapped
over with iron at the foot, and it must be a clever mouse
indeed who finds a hole through which he may obtain
admission.

Barn and machine-room occupy the second floor of the
central building, a great door opening from it over the mowhay, from whence fodder will be taken in.   The granary is
disconnected from the open roof by a solid plaster partition,
which is designed to prevent rats, that may be brought in
with the corn, from getting into the granary.   In the machine-
room we find another original idea of Mr. Berriman's, which
practical experience has commended, in the shape of an iron
cage of the outline of a crinoline, which holds the wool while
it is weighed.

The granary is partitioned off with matchboarding, ploughed
and tongued, and bound with sheet iron at the foot—so
determined is the owner to keep his castle impregnable against
his small, but mischievous enemy.   In divided apartments are
oats, oil cake, bran, maize, and barley stores, for cattle sheds,
poultry yard and piggery.   The partitions of the corn hutch

may, by an ingenious arrangement, be brought back to the
door of the granary, if additional storage is required for the
grain.   One more precaution against the rodents.   The steps
leading to the hatches of the wool-loft are movable, and when
the farm-hand has descended from the loft he draws them
up by a novel hoist, so that neither rat nor mouse shall have
any assistance in ascending to the upper chamber.

The loft leads to quite a pleasant surprise for the visitor.
The north end of the building directly faces Clovelly, and
Mr. Berriman takes too keen a delight in the beauties of
Nature not to have availed himself of the pleasure of contemplating the magnificent landscape which this afforded.
Leading the way to the loft, he opens the door at the gable
end and emerges on a spacious balcony, commanding splendid
views of Gallantry Bower, the Wilderness and the Bristol
Channel, with all the grand expanse of land and sea, which
may be surveyed with a good telescope on a fine day, when
the sunshine bathes Clovelly Court in a splendour beyond its
own.   Here in this cool corner, hidden from the sun's hottest
rays, a summer siesta may be enjoyed under the most agreeable circumstances.   But we are not summer visitors, and our
orders are of the " marching " class.

We have done with the buildings, and must now spend a
hour in the fields, or the more practical lessons which the
Highford Farm has for agriculturists will be overlooked.   Mr.
Berriman has constructed lanes leading to his lower fields, and
as we pass through these we learn that his experience at
Highford has led him to a second venture in reclaiming waste
land.   At Forda, in Bradworthy parish, he has acquired
ninety-three acres, which he is adapting to grazing and corn

growing purposes. Throughout the fields at Highford there
is a luxuriant growth of grass even to-day, the whole land
which literally bore nothing worthy the farmer's attention
being now permanent pasture of a rich type.

The system of the fountains in the fields is simple but
effective. Under a pointed arch recess, of brick and stone,
a trough of Dartmoor granite is placed, and beside it a ball
tap in a small cistern, with wood cover. As the cattle drink
the water in the trough, the water in the little cistern falls
and the ball falls with it, opening the tap which admits a
fresh supply. The third field in a northerly direction brings
the visitor to the edge of Highford Wood, and as the slope
has been traversed, Gallantry Bower, the Wilderness, and the
Bristol Channel have still been in view.

At the foot of the wood, which Mr. Berriman intends
to preserve intact, as a charming feature of the landscape,
is a miniature Watersmeet. A streamlet running to the east
from Hartland joins another purling brook running north and
dividing Clovelly from Hartland. By-and-bye their dun waters
will empty themselves into the salt sea. Mr. Berriman
possesses eleven acres of wood, and his good taste has not
deserted him in his decision to make it an ornamental fringe
to his property. Higher and Lower Valley, and the properties
of Parson Edgecombe and Mr. Pitts-Tucker, of Barnstaple,
are the northern boundaries of Highford.

Ascending to the farm again, the natural advantage of which
Mr. Berriman has availed himself in arranging his water supply
is observed. There is a gradual slope upward to the highway
on the northern side. From the bog reservoir to the buildings
there is a fall of 18 feet. The subterranean chamber which

carried off the water from the quarry was dug 12 feet deep.
Making a personal visit to the reservoir, the future visitor
will be startled by some pleasantly surprising effects, which
would suggest that Mr. Berriman has been a diligent student of
Scott's "Kenilworth," and has put into practice some of the
quaint aquatic conceits the Earl of Leicester devised out of
compliment to Queen Bess.   The place of bogs has been
effectively drained, and at the foot of the first slope Mr.
Berriman is making a fish-pond, which will begin at the bridge
of stout masonry which he has thrown over the streamlet that
murmurs through what is now a pleasant vale.   Approaching
the massive gateway erected upon the bridge, as if at the
touch of a fairy wand, fountains begin to play in the scalloped
terra cotta basins on each tall pillar of the gateway.   By-and-
bye, when Mr. Berriman has completed his harmless sorceries,
the imagination will raise this picture to a peep into enchanted
land.

At length we have come, by another field, to the railed-off
reservoir, which is used, as has been already explained, for
draining the dry fields and supplying the farm and fountains.
The roof is semi-circular in appearance, with brick abutments
on either side, and an arcaded entrance.   Over the iron-bound
door the simple inscription appears on the key-stone of the
arch, "J.B., 1884,"—the author and the date of the completion of an important branch of this highly successful
experiment in the reclamation of waste land.   The supply
appears inexhaustible, the spring being permanent, having
survived the severe test of 1887.   There is a filter for the
water supplied to the house and farm, but no such precaution
is, of course, necessary with the drainage water.   At the

intake a foot or two above the reservoir itself, an ingenious arrangement is seen, the object being the cleaning out of the reservoir. There are two sluices, one admitting the water into the reservoir pipe, and the other carrying the supply off, at an acute angle, to the stream below. By shutting the reservoir sluice and opening that of the stream, the huge tank may be drained of the supply and then thoroughly cleaned.

But this supply is, of course, unavailable on the south side of Hartland road, to which Mr. Berriman's property extends. This is where the work of reclamation commenced, the spot nearest the moorland being now a very productive vegetable garden. When draining the land Mr. Berriman, observing the course of the strata, remarked that there was a soft strata running in one direction, and calculated that where it was intersected by a hard strata there the water would force itself, and, by natural causes, be driven toward the surface. He called in the well-sinkers and ordered them to dig a well in the spot arrived at by his geological calculation. The work-men saw not these signs, and advised Mr. Berriman that he had selected the wrong spot. "There is no water here," said they. "Never mind, dig!" was the reply, "it will be my fault if there is none, not yours." And they dug. But not for long. The water soon came in a good and persistent stream.

The first use of this spring is to supply a fountain in the field next the road and a tank which acts in a three-fold capacity—as a reservoir for the fountain in the garden below, a supply for a fountain to the field on the opposite side of the hedge, and another ball-tap trough in the field below. The garden which is at the extremity of the property was a literal

M

morass, and its cultivation was despaired of by everyone save
Mr. Berriman.   But to-day he grows fine heads of cabbage
upon it, seakale, spinach, vegetable marrows, cucumbers,
turnips, leeks, onions, peas, and potatoes.   There is a little
summer-house facing the sunny south, and overlooking a pretty
fountain, which plays in fantastic gladiatorial fashion.   This,
and the liquid manure tank in the garden, are supplied from
the reservoir in the field above.   Clearly defined is the
" scientific frontier " between this splendidly cultivated property and the moorland just a few yards away. Money, manure,
" elbow-grease " and brains have made all the difference.

What has been accomplished by this attempt at model
farming ? In the first place the market value of the land has
been raised 800 per cent. at the least.   The produce of the
property has been increased in proportion.   A disgrace to
English agriculture has been converted into a credit.   It has
been shown that sound common sense, backed up by means,
enterprise, determination, and a firm regard for natural laws,
can accomplish much in the cultivation of the land.   But we
have not yet seen the full fruition of Mr. Berriman's plan.
His farm will be a model in many more senses ere a great
number of years have passed.   His dairy will supply the New
Inn at Clovelly with the Devonshire delicacies of butter and
cream throughout the summer.   Mr. Berriman's stock will be
heard of in the cattle markets ere long, and possibly among
the prize winners at our local and county shows.   And the
parish of Hartland will boast a farm to be proud of in
Highford, with its splendid buildings and luxuriously green
fields.

But we must remember that Mr. Berriman is landlord

and tenant in one. No "unearned increment" disturbs his day dreams of improvement. He marches on with the confidence that he will have the full benefit of his outlay. There will be no taxation of improvement in increased rents. We see what can be done in the reclamation of the waste land of the country. Highford in Hartland and Forda in Bradworthy, working in combination, will be quoted as examples of what *must* be done *if* "the bold peasantry, a country's pride," are to be retained in England. When the land laws deal fairly as between man and man, intensive cultivation, such as that described in this article, will become more general, and Mr. Berriman will have earned the distinction of being a pioneer in model farming.

XIV.—THE MARLAND TERRA-COTTA, BRICK AND STONEWARE PIPE WORKS, TORRINGTON.

" Marland bricks " is as familiar a term in the mouths of the modern builder of the Western Counties as household words. Marland terra cotta is fast making a cosmopolitan reputation for itself. The two manufactures, carried on under one extended roof at Marland Clay Moor, employ 75 hands. Apart from the interest of the industry, there are obvious reasons why this series of articles would be imcomplete if it failed to include the important manufactory at Marland. To the superficial observer it may appear that brick-making is an ignoble occupation and one entirely lacking in attractiveness. Setting aside the wisdom of Carlyle, who reminds us that " Not a *brick* was made without some man having had to think of the making of that *brick*," we must remember that they are connecting links

M 2

in the history of the most remote ages of man.   The brick was the earliest invention of the potter's art.   When the lordly Egyptian despised the rude hut, plastered with clay to protect it against the sun or storm, the necessity of symmetrical buildings produced the brick.   Brick-making as an occupation has descended with various modifications from the building of the Tower of Babel to the present day.   It is essential, in the first place, that bricks should be symmetrical, and their form is generally rectangular.   From their geometrical shape, they have preserved the canon of ancient measure.   Bricks were manufactured at a remote period of antiquity by the Egyptians, the Babylonians and the Assyrians, and some of them being inscribed with written characters have been of priceless value in conveying historic facts to the present age.   The Egyptian bricks were called *teba*, meaning box, from the small wooden box or mould from which they were turned out—a mode of manufacture that survives in brick-making by hand to-day. One of the most interesting inscriptions with which bricks have been stamped, thereby elevating them to the dignity of historic monuments, is that of the prænomen of Thothmes III., who reigned about 1400 years before Christ.   The bricks of Egypt illuminate the sacred page, their composition of straw and clay witnessing to the truth of Scripture : " Ye shall no more give the people straw to make brick, as heretofore : let them go and gather straw for themselves."—*Exodus v, 7.*

A large number of Roman bricks bore the name of the Roman consuls.   The proud nobility of the " eternal city " did not despise " trade," for they derived their revenues from the kilns of their Campanian and Sabine farms.

The history of brick-making in England begins with the

Plate 21 (above) Peters Marland Clay Mines about 1900 showing pit head gear and 3ft gauge works railway; *22 (below)* open cast clay pit at Peters Marland about 1910

HUXTABLE'S PATENT EXPANDING HORSE RAKE.

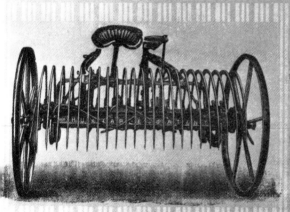

Patent Rake contracted to 7 feet, with Teeth 2½ ins. apart for Clean Raking.

PATENT LAZY TONG
FOR ALTERING THE PITCH OF TEE OF HUXTABLE'S HORSE RAKE

THE method employed fo altering the width of th Teeth is simple and perfect—by a series of Lazy tongs firml screwed together and capable of any expansion. The movemen of these is so little that th joints will last a lifetime withou perceptive wear, and, when pu together, form a combination of strength unobtainable by an other method.

Plate 23 (above) Huxtable's Patent Expanding Horse Rake; *24 (below* an old horse-drawn 'Star' plough still in the yard at the back of the works at South Molten

Roman invasion. About A.D. 44 bricks were made in England by the Romans, and in A.D. 866 by the Anglo Saxons under King Alfred, the patron of learning and industry. Under King Henry VIII. and Elizabeth the manufactures greatly flourished. The size was regulated, with Act of Parliament, by King Charles I. in 1625.

Terra-cotta is not far in the rear of the ancient brick in point of antiquity. When the invention of the mould brought to perfection the art of producing the master-pieces of early art in a small form and in a rapid and cheap manner, then terra-cottas flooded the market, the manufactures of antiquity being as numerous as the plaster casts sold by the Italian itinerants of to-day.

From this brief historical retrospect we return to our subject proper with heightened interest. It is a pleasant drive, encircling the wooded hills, and rising to heights commanding extensive views of a fair country, that takes us from the Torrington terminus of the London and South Western Railway to the Marland Terra Cotta and Brick Works. A light railway line, six miles in extent, exists for the conveyance of clay and the manufactures of the Marland Works to the South Western Company's station. Through a famous hunting country, of which the Gribble Inn, a popular " meet," is the centre, we run to Yarde, a little hamlet less than a mile from the works, where a foreman's residence and sixteen workmen's cottages— built, of course, of Marland brick—have been erected for the accommodation of the employés. Between Yarde and Marland Clay Moor we pass Winscott, the pleasant residence of J. C Moore-Stevens, Esq., that stands on a wooded eminence which overlook the extensive property of the Squire.

A gentle descent brings us to the entrance to the Moor. In the centre of over a hundred acres of clayey soil rises the tall stack of the works, and round it cluster the kilns and the workshops of Mr. J. W. Ludlam, the enterprising proprietor of the industry, in whose hands it has been for six years. The works themselves, although most compactly arranged, cover three acres. They are situate in Marland parish, and lie in a hollow of the gently undulating country. A stream bounds the property and divides it from Merton parish, whose church spire on the hill-top above the works is gilded by the last rays of the departing sun.

But a word of the "raw material" ere we enter the works themselves. The Marland clay-pits produce a variety of plastic earth. "Fat" clay, "sandy" clay, "fire" clay, and "yellow" clay are the technical descriptions, and these varieties are sub-divided into secondaries and tertiaries. In colours the brick and terra-cotta maker has a choice extending from white, through every shade of buff, pink and "pinky buff," "straw-berry red," and in every shade of red, to the richest and ruddiest "Queen Anne." Thousands of tons of clay have been taken from the Marland Moor; millions of tons remain; so that posterity will not lack for material ready to hand for the exercise of the plastic arts, and scientists need not yet discuss a fusion which will produce clay.

From the clay-pits we make our way to the boiler-house of the works and see the motive power which has replaced the slaves of the Egyptians in the modern manufacture of bricks. A Galloway boiler and a compound tubular patent together supply a maximum of 100 h.p., though the boilers are worked at a pressure of 50 h.p. The machinery of the works is of a first-class character and embraces not a few improvements of modern invention. A Plowright's Condenser and engine, by Musgrave, of Bolton, and another engine by Nicholls, of Leeds, together provide a driving power of 70 h.p., the fly-wheels being, respectively, 14 and 12 feet. It is worthy of remark that the fitting of the machinery was all done on the spot, "Devon" being the motto of Mr. Ludlam.

Before entering the works the reservoirs were noticed. By an ingenious arrangement Mr. Ludlam has cleverly obviated the possibility of his water supply running short in the summer months. From one of two large reservoirs on the Moor, the water supply is conveyed to a water tower at the height of the roof of the works, whence it passes, through five-inch pipes, to the boilers. Then, from the steam condenser, it returns when it has done its work, through five and six-inch pipes into another tower, from whence, by the application of the principle of specific gravity, it is made to flow up to the receiving reservoir. Eighty feet of shafting connects all the machinery with the boilers, and the shafts are manufactured of steel.

Now to discover how the brick is made. The clay is brought up the incline from the pits by a chain trolley, the contents of which are tipped on to a platform upon the highest shelf of the brick-making block. The clay then passes through a pair of rollers, drops into a perforated pan, is ground under a pair of edge-runners, weighing three tons each, and is then forced through a perforated bottom by a pair of rollers which would turn the weigh-bridge at 25 cwt. It is next forced out by three arms, placed under the pans, to a pair of compression rollers, which pass the now plastic clay into a machine pug, after being ground in which it is pushed out on to the brick cutting tables—two of Murray's patent—the wires cutting twenty at a time. In this way it is possible to manufacture 40,000 bricks a day here, the average output being 25,000. The brick making machinery is of the double delivery principle. The gearing is all new and of the latest pattern.

Three of the operations of brick-making have been accomplished. The brick earth has been prepared, tempered and moulded. The bricks remain to be dried and burnt. But as these operations are common to all the manufactures of the works, it will be of interest to turn aside for a moment and to contrast with the modern process that which prevailed 1,400 B.C.—that is, some 3,300 years ago. A most instructive representation of the art of brick-making is depicted in the tomb of Rekmora, an officer of Thothmes III., of 1,400 B.C. The picture is explained as follows : Labourers are first seen mixing with their hoes, mud, clay, or alluvial soil, to a proper consistency, the water being brought from a tank constructed for the purpose and protected from too rapid an evaporation by the lotus within it and the trees planted round it. Other labourers are carrying the water thence in large jars to supply brickmakers. When sufficiently kneaded the clay is transferred to the pans and thrown down in a heap before the brickmaker, who stamps them out of a mould and then lays them in single rows to dry in the sun. When ready for drying, or for the furnace, they were carried, like modern pails, suspended on poles. Six of them appears to have been a man's load. The occupation was not much to the taste of the employed, for the stick (or the lash) seems to have been liberally used. The inscriptions on the picture record that they are bricks made by royal captives, or slaves, for the building of the temple of

Amen Ra at Thebes. Although it became an ignoble occupation, traces of the ancient importance of brickmaking appear
in the ceremony of Tahraka, B.C. 715—658, the Ethiopian
ruler being represented at Medina Habos, employed on his
knees in making bricks.

The terra-cotta clay is treated in quite a different manner
to the brick clay. In a 10-feet pan, rollers of two tons each,
worked by a portable engine of 20 horse power, are grinding
the various clays thoroughly, to the consistency of flour. The
different terra-cotta tints are gained by mixtures of clays,which
is a piece of Marland "freemasonry." Waiving our curiosity
we learn that all waste brickbats and burnt material is employed in the manufacture of terra-cotta and that of various
vitreous bricks.

Overhead the manufacture of terra-cotta is carried on. In
this department we are fortunate to arrive during the execution
of some artistic work designed for the Forester's Hall at
Cowes, Isle of Wight. Architectural terra-cotta has now
become one of the principal manufactures of the works, and we
have here an instance of the elegance of the ornamental work
which Marland has contributed to the beautification of modern
buildings. The symbolical design before us, in which the
emblem of the Foresters' benefit society is wrought in the
enduring clay, is an instance of the capabilities of the art
in building decoration. The subject is a forester binding
sticks, and the arms and symbols of the Court are faithfully
reproduced in terra-cotta. Corbels, trusses, capitals, balustra-
ding, terminals, pier caps, key-stones, string-courses, air bricks,
enriched string-courses and panelling, ornamental finials,
window-dressings, door-heads, architraves and pediments, gable

coping, arch blocks, and chimney tops—in multitudinous
design and of artistic draughtsmanship all these varieties
of architectural terra-cotta are being supplied to-day for
the decoration of some of the finest buildings.

The fact that Mr. Alma Tadema, R.A., has entrusted
to Mr. Ludlam a commission in terra-cotta decorations for his
own studio, the eminent painter having modelled some of the
choice " bits " with his own hands, has its peculiar significance
as a tribute to the natural advantages of Marland terra-cotta
and the excellence of its manufacture.   For the mansions
on the Earl of Cadogan's estate in Pont Street, Chelsea, extensive orders are being executed in architectural terra-cotta, and
the front elevation of these handsome residences will be a
tribute to the artistic worth of the Marland manufacture.   The
Surbiton New Assembly Rooms is largely decorated with these
architectural ornaments, and mansions at Brighton and in
London have had their attractions heightened by a liberal use
of this terra-cotta in their construction.   Terra-cotta vases are,
of course, a prominent manufacture at Marland.   The manufacture of terra-cotta is, of course, the most artistic side of the
industry.   The draughtsman receives the architect's drawings,
and takes out full size working drawings, which are then
handed to the foreman model maker.   It is his office to reproduce them in plaster models for the use of the mould-makers,
who take their moulds from the models ; the moulds, in turn,
are passed to the pressers.   When "black-hard" the mould is
touched up by the modellers.   The terra-cotta, when taken
from the presses, is gradually dried for three weeks, the firing
following ; it is a week in the kiln.   Marland terra-cotta is
made of the best stone ware and vitrified clays, is non-absorbent,

has a clean, smooth surface, and possesses all the enduring qualities of pottery. Nearly £4,000 worth was supplied for the New City of Exeter Asylum, and beside the instances we have already mentioned, the Fountain Memorial to the late Earl of Sandwich at Huntingdon, the Conservative Club at Watford, large mills at Hemel Hempstead, villas and shops at Paignton, and mansions in the West End, have Marland terra-cotta for their architectural decorations. Coming nearer home, we may add Mr. Vaughan's mansion at Torrington and the Ilfracombe Shelter and Arcade to the list. Twenty-five men are employed in the terra-cotta department over the brick-flues, to which we will now return.

There are three large sets of flues for drying purposes at the Marland works, and the waste heat at the top of the kilns, of which there are fifteen in all, is utilised. The " continuous kiln " is the new principle adopted by Mr. Ludlam, and by this arrangement 270,000 bricks can be fired at one time. The kilns are heated with coals of the best quality. Balance lifts convey the bricks to and from the top of the kiln, for drying purposes. In addition to the great circular kiln, there are five large square and round kilns, chiefly employed in the firing of terra-cotta. The flues are connected, and when the fire has played through and burnt the bricks from end to end of the kilns, the heat is carried off to dry bricks elsewhere, so that it is drying two or three chambers and burning one at the same time. The continuous kiln is intersected with tunnels, which are used for drying bricks. Passing through these dark chambers, with fierce fires ever and anon luridly lighting the gloom, we have an imaginative glimpse at Dante's "Inferno."

Not all the bricks are made by machinery, for here, in the

terra-cotta loft, are three men, making, by hand, a special large brick for the Barnstaple Water Company. Up to this point we have had no classification of the Marland bricks, and this may now be conveniently supplied. There are facing bricks, in white, buff, grey and Bath stone colours. They are made, in shapes as varied as their colours, for moulding and facing work. It is claimed for them as their advantageous peculiarities that they are non-absorbent and frost-proof. London is the principal market for this manufacture, although the demand of the provinces is growing in measure. They have the preference of the builder in sound of Bow bells on account of their clean and smooth surface, and are largely used in lieu of glazed bricks for underground subways, stores, &c. Liverpool, Belfast and Dublin builders have also shewn a partiality for this brick, with which, by the way, the glove factory of Mr. W. Vaughan, and his elegant mansion, are faced, together with villas at Ilfracombe, Barnstaple, and the Mid-Devon Hotel, at Ashbury. Another speciality is the " granite " vitrified bricks, of the texture of stone-ware, which, being unaffected by the strongest acid or alkalis, are impervious to moisture, and will resist a more than average crushing pressure. This is an entirely new manufacture, and as a proof that it has supplied a felt want in its peculiar adaptation to engineering works, the fact that nearly a million have recently been used in the construction of large waterworks at Kew for the Grand Junction Canal Company may be cited. It is interesting to learn that they have been selected by the engineers of the Barnstaple and Ilfracombe new water-works now in course of construction. For docks, reservoirs, bridges, and sewers, it is asserted that these bricks possess

a superiority over every other manufacture. " Granite vitrified " is the term also applied to the paving bricks made
at Marland, and largely used in the streets at Torrington,
Barnstaple, Bideford, Taunton, Penzance, Okehampton, and
Holsworthy. They are made in a variety of patterns and have
grooves designed for securing a firm foothold and for carrying
off all water, leaving a perfectly dry surface on a paved walk.
Buff and grey are the colours in which they are manufactured.
This paving is said to be imperishable and much cheaper than
stone, and its advantages for stables, coach-houses, yards,
wharves, breweries, railway platforms, public streets and
terraces have led to its extensive use. The approaches to
Lord's cricket ground are paved with Marland paviors ; at
Olympia they have also made their appearance ; whilst the
London General Omnibus Company have used the bricks in
their stables, and the London and South Western Railway
Company lately employed them in paving their platforms. At
Hereford these Marland bricks came into competition with
their old Staffordshire rivals, for street-paving purposes, and
were preferred before them. " Advance Marland ! " say all
that have the success of our local industries at heart.

A word of other features of the works and manufactures at
Marland and we have done. To finish the catalogue of the
productions of Mr. Ludlam, fire bricks and fire clay goods generally must be mentioned in a paragraph with the brown glazed
stoneware bricks of the firm. The fire bricks contain nearly
90 per cent. of silica, and are, accordingly, specially adapted
for use in gas works, lime kilns, smelting and welding furnaces.
It suffices to say that Her Majesty's Government have been
supplied with these goods for dockyard purposes. In Plymouth

New Markets brown-glazed bricks are largely used for the butchers' stalls, their bright and imperishable surface-glaze admitting of their being easily washed. London contractors have also shewn themselves alive to the advantages of this variety of brick.

Fitters' and blacksmith's shops, offices and stables complete the round of the works, of which Mr. J. M. Limpus is the general manager. The foreman of brick works and engineer is Mr. Wood, and the chief draughtsman in the terra-cotta department, Mr. Norman. Bideford is the shipping port of the works, so that, with its light railway to the main line which runs by the river side, this interesting industry is not so isolated as it seems there by the clay pits on Marland Moor.

XV.—RALEIGH CABINET WORKS. BARNSTAPLE.

On the memorable night of the 5th of March, 1888, the Raleigh Cabinet Works of Messrs. Shapland and Petter were burnt to the ground. To-day, at the Bridge End Wharf, Barnstaple, an imposing pile of workshops has been erected on either side of the familiar footpath leading to Anchor Wood. In recording that dire disaster we expressed the general hope that the manufactory upon which the welfare of so large a portion of the industrial population of the town depended would rise, Phœnix-like, from its ashes, and that, in its re-establishment, it would excel the predecessor works in the character of the manufactures, and in its labour-employing capacities. Public expectations have been realised and far out-distanced. A year has not yet passed since Barnstaple awoke to a knowledge of the calamity which had befallen hundreds of its toiling citizens and nobly responded to the demand which the disaster made upon its practical sympathy. And yet there now exist works of a description and extent which have cast the old manufactory of Raleigh in the shade. It is unnecessary to comment upon the resolution, energy, and enterprise of the firm. The facts speak for themselves, and in this, one of the last of our series of articles, we shall have many interesting and significant facts to disclose.

Until, in reporting the great Raleigh fire, we described the history of the works, few of the public were familiar with the attractive record of the growth of the industry from very small beginnings. Half-a-century since the senior partner of the present firm was with Mr. Crook, a cabinet-maker of considerable local repute. Mr. Shapland proceeded to London, and later on took what was then considered the serious step of a voyage to America. Whilst in the land of modern mechanical invention, Mr. Shapland's attention was attracted to a machine-made moulding. A few months later, Mr. Shapland reproduced it in England, himself preparing the patterns of the castings. The first piece of this remarkable wavy moulding is said never to have been improved upon.

It is a maxim in commerce that all great enterprises have small beginnings. Mr. Shapland commenced business in one only of the rooms at Raleigh factory, which at that time was used as a woollen factory. About this time Mr. H. Petter retired from the great publishing firm, afterwards known as Cassell, Petter, and Galpin, at La Belle Sauvage Yard, Ludgate, and returned to Barnstaple. He was for a time connected with the *North Devon Journal*, as part proprietor of the paper, subsequently entering into partnership with Mr Shapland, in the cabinet making business.

The removal of the firm to premises in Bear Street marked the development of the concern.   The new moulding was here applied to general cabinet work.   From this time forward the history of the business was one of gradual, persistent growth, until it attained the proportions which were for the first time wholly revealed to the general public on the eve of its entire destruction.

The removal from Bear Street to Raleigh Factory occurred twenty-five years ago.   At that embryo stage of the industry, it appeared highly improbable that the large number of spacious rooms would be all required.   But, as time passed on and the business developed, they were everyone eventually occupied, and then the need arose for enlargement.   From period to period the workshops were added to, until the greater portion of the property had been utilised, when the fatal fire of March last reduced the mass of buildings to the bare walls of the larger sections.

The growth of the Raleigh Cabinet Factory was con-temporary with the application of machinery to its manu-factures.   Up to 1878, cabinet-making had taken somewhat of this order : the wood was sawn out and some of the rougher work done by machinery, in addition to mouldings, turning, &c.

A decade since the trade passed through a critical period of its existence.   America had applied machinery to many operations of cabinet-making, and English tradesmen were not slow in awaking to the advantages of the inventions of " cute

Jonathan." Messrs. Shapland and Petter were among the firms who resolved to avail themselves of these great labour-saving appliances. They gave instructions to the agent of Messrs. J. A. Fay and Co., of Cincinnati, Ohio, to fit up a most complete set of wood-working machinery. From the time of this bold step to the day of the calamitous fire of 1888, Messrs. Shapland and Petter were continually adding novelties in machinery peculiar to their manufactures as soon as the ingenuity of the inventive mind had sought out and produced " some new thing." When it is remembered that mechanical agencies have now been applied to almost every part of the work—from the cutting out of the wood to the point where the different parts of the furniture are placed in the cabinet-maker's hands, ready for him to " clean off" and " put together "—the enterprise and the outlay which the determination of the Raleigh firm involved may be understood. " Nothing succeeds like success," and our readers who evinced such intense interest in the accounts which we published of the disaster last year aré familiar with the flourishing condition of the business previous to the great losses then inflicted upon the partners. One circumstance which heightened the extent of the calamity was the fact that the manufactured stock was abnormally large, to the tune of many thousands of pounds, in consequence of the spring orders having been prepared for delivery in April.

Barnstaple thoroughly appreciated the crisis of March, 1888. If Messrs. Shapland and Petter had then succumbed to circumstances, the town must inevitably have lost one of its principal industries. But one item of information which we published at the time inspired hope and acted as an

N

antidote to the general depression.   Almost ere the lurid glare
had departed from the ruins which had replaced a splendid
industry—when silence and darkness had fallen upon the
scene of the busy hum of machinery and the movement of
clever craftsmen plying their decorative arts—ere the Raleigh
Cabinet Works was irretrievably a thing of the past, the
foundation stone of the new manufactory had, in a sense,
been laid.   Messages had been flashed to America, by the
Atlantic cable, securing machinery which it was impossible
to obtain in the Old Country, and orders were given at home
for all the necessities of a new industry.   Thus, by prompt and
decisive action, the after-effect of the calamity was averted.
The diversion of the trade of the firm into other channels was
prevented.   If there had been any delay, the valued staff of
workmen would have drifted hither and thither, with consequences fatal to the industry and derogatory to Barnstaple's
commercial prosperity.   Messrs. Shapland and Petter left
nothing undone that should have been done to prevent such
a catastrophe.   Before many days had elapsed after the fire,
the immediate completion of plans already formed for the
erection of a manufactory at the Bridge Wharf was resolved
upon, the scale and character of the new works, however,
undergoing a revolution as the result of the unforeseen
occurrence.

   Only about a year before the destruction of the Raleigh
factory Messrs. Shapland and Petter had purchased a ship-
building yard, previously in the occupation of Mr. Westacott,
and several acres of freehold land adjoining.   It was this
provision that enabled the firm to recommence their business
within a remarkably brief period.   The inhabitants have

watched the erection of the well-planned buildings with the greatest interest, and have learnt with marked satisfaction that in its restoration the industry will eclipse the factory whose destruction is marked with letters of fire in their diary of 1888. The new works are not yet completed. Their extension by the side of the railway line to the limit of the land acquired by the firm is shortly contemplated.

The interest of this article will chiefly depend upon the description of the modern machinery, original inventions and admirable general arrangements of the factory. Little time or space can be spared upon any description of cabinet-making, from which we may be the readier excused because of the familiarity of every household with the productions of the trade. " Cabinet-maker," formerly applied to one whose occupation it was to make cabinets or receptacles for curiosities and valuables, is now an inclusive term, more widely used in reference to a maker of household furniture in general. By " cabinet " our forefathers understood a piece of furniture containing drawers or compartments in which to keep curiosities and other articles of value. Says Swift :

> In vain the workman showed his wit,
> With rings and hinges counterfeit,
> To make it seem, in this disguise,
> A *cabinet* to vulgar eyes.

The derivation of the word has illustration in the governmental Cabinet ; but the " green-eyed monster " need not cause the workman to look upon the Ministerial meeting with jaundiced eye ; never such an uncomplimentary couplet was written of his trade as Moore penned of the politicians, in his satirical *Twopenny Post-Bag, Sale of the Tools :*

> Excepting for cabinet-making, I doubt
> For that delicate purpose, they're rather worn out.

N 2

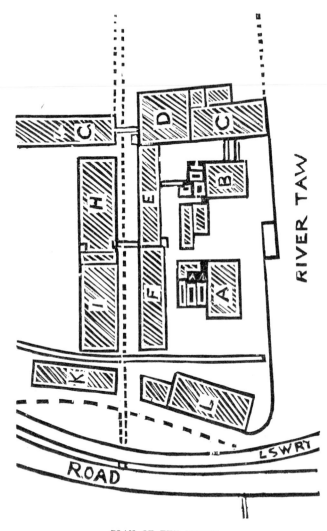

PLAN OF THE WORKS.

The rough ground plan of the Works which we reproduce above, from a block prepared upon the spot, will
assist those of our readers who have not been privileged
to pay a visit to them in following our description of the
new and modern manufactory. The first feature of the works
which is likely to impress the visitor is their division into
several distinct blocks which, for convenience sake, are
lettered as shewn on the plan. The reasons which weighed
with Messrs. Shapland and Petter in their adoption of this
style of building are obvious when the cause of the complete
demolition of the old factory is remembered.   The new
buildings are very substantial, all the floors being either of
concrete or of solid planks of timber three inches thick without any apertures to serve as flues for fire.   The staircases
and lift-wells, without exception, are either outside the walls
or independent of the various floors and buildings.

A complete system of water supply is another admirable
precaution. Ten hydrants are located in different parts of
the premises.   On the landings of the workshops hose is
attached to the pipe in readiness for use, the hydrants in
the buildings being independent of the water supply.   In each
room several buckets filled with water are standing, and one
workman is especially told off to see that they are at all times
in position and full.   The " Grinnel Automatic Sprinkler "
is the preventive means adopted in the portions of the
building in which there is the greatest risk of an outbreak
of fire.   The action of the " Sprinkler " is simple and effective.
An easily fusible stopper is liberated on a moderate rise above
the normal temperature of the room in which it is placed.
The water then flows in a spreading stream from the tank

above the roof of the block of buildings and floods the place which is the scene of the outbreak. Messrs. Shapland and Petter have subjected the patent to a practical test, and found it to be all that the patentees claim for it.

The electric light is another element of safety. The whole of the workshops are lit with this brilliant and safe illuminant; and a pretty and novel sight it is to catch, from across the river, a glimpse of the whole block aglow with the light which electricity has given us. Another very interesting and ingenious safeguard, aptly styled "the Cyclone," merits a passing word by reason of its originality. Through tubes carried to each planing machine in that workshop which has scarcely an equal in its mechanical appointments, throughout the whole of Europe, the sawdust is drawn by a current of air developed by the rapid revolution of a fan placed outside the workshop, and is conveyed across the yard to a huge funnel-shaped vessel, which deposits it in the central dust chamber. Thus all the more inflammable litter of the workshops is taken out of danger's way, and the safety of the premises thereby materially increased. The various blocks of buildings are connected with iron bridges, and the doors of the workshops are lined with galvanized iron, which the Fire Insurance Companies hold to be a greater preventive even than the provision of iron doors, inasmuch as the former will not warp with the heat—a disadvantage of the iron door. Underneath block B are water tanks, the reservoirs being co-extensive with the ground floor of the block itself.

To make assurance doubly sure, the plan of the buildings is further in evidence, on the subject of the reduction of risk. Blocks A and B, it will be observed, are completely detached, whilst C, D, E and F, apparently adjoin each other. As a matter of fact, however, they are almost as effectually divided as are A and B. They are separated by thick walls, or, in those parts where openings are necessary, by double iron doors. And these parti-walls, it should be added, invariably extend up through the roof, forming parapets. In this way these three blocks are also made separate from a fire-risk standpoint. In the corner of D block, and adjoining E, is a steam lift for passengers and goods. Two other lifts, of a similar character, are provided in different parts of the works. With these lifts, and with the iron bridges connecting different parts of the establishment, it is also as obvious that, although divided as regards the danger of the spread of a conflagration occurring at either point, they still are intimately connected for the transit of goods and other purposes.

In taking a bird's-eye view of the factory the adaptation of the site to the purposes for which Messrs. Shapland & Petter have acquired it must be apparent to the least observant mind. With the river on one side and the rail on the other, the firm have two great advantages of their trade at their very doors. That they are not neglecting the facilities of the site is apparent from the fact that they have, on the river bank, built a sea wall with a slip—a very arduous undertaking, from the marshy character of the bank, by the way. A good wharf is the reward of this piece of forethought and enterprise. Neither has the advantage of the propinquity of the line of the London and South Western Railway Company been neglected. The Company have arranged to lay down a siding connecting the works with their system. This siding, which is shewn in the plan, will run in front of the saw mills. The raw material from the ship's side may be deposited by it at the saw mills, and again received, in the metamorphosed form of finished furniture, from the stores on the other side of the premises for transit to London and elsewhere.

Now to deal with the block of buildings in greater detail. A is the newly-erected saw mill in front of which the logs, coming by sea or rail, will be deposited. It will contain saw frames, circular saws, band saws, and a saw-sharpening machine. The most remarkable machine will be a " log band saw,"—the first of its kind ever introduced into this country. Its special purpose is the sawing of logs up to 5 feet in diameter, at a rapid speed. A central railway will run through the saw mills, bringing and taking away the wood with despatch. Block B is its second destination, and we will follow it there. Here are the new drying kilns where the wood is perfectly seasoned in from six to twelve days. This is a cleverly-devised and most effectual arrangement, and its time and labour-saving capabilities may be judged from the fact that, under the old process, from one to two years would be consumed in this operation. The extent of the works and their interest lays upon us the injunction to be brief even in the description of new and original features. The principle of the drying kilns, then, in a few words, is this : The wood is carefully stacked in air-tight chambers admitting of their being kept at a uniform temperature of 120 degrees. These chambers are lined with absorbent felt which obviously assists the operation. Along one of the top angles of the room runs a large slotted tube, a similar arrangement being observable at the opposite bottom angle. After the wood has been " sweated " for some hours, by the injection of steam into the chamber, circulation is " set up " by

powerful fans.   The top tube sucks out the moist air and it
is drawn by the fans through condensing cylinders, which are
filled with coils of pipes through which cold water is forced at
a great pressure.   The condensed moisture drops to the bottom
of the cylinder and escapes, whilst the air, thus rid of its
moisture, is hurried back, through the lower tube again, into
the rooms, once more to be sucked out at the top, laden with
moisture,   The circulation which we have described goes on
many thousands of times a day, and continues until all the
moisture is extracted and the wood is dry.

The block A A, adjoining the saw mills, contains the
motive power of machinery and electric light.   It accommodates two boilers, an engine of the old type and one of the
new.   Outside this a very large and powerful " Lancashire"
boiler with " Galloway " cross-tubes, 30 feet by 8 feet, is now
in course of being fitted up.   In B B we find a fine tubular
boiler of the locomotive type, and a very powerful engine
which is a complete departure from the ordinary methods.   It
is capable of developing 100 horse-power and has a high initial
speed of 200 revolutions per minute, and this is multiplied until,
as we shall see further on, some of the cutters make a revolution
of 6,000 per minute.   This new type of engine invites description by its interesting character ;   space will not, however,
permit of details being given.   But in the adjoining block we
come upon another engine of the same type, running at a
speed of 300 revolutions per minute in comparative silence.   It
is designed to run at this speed night and day, for a considerable time, without stopping.   This is rendered possible by the
inclusion in its mechanism of a special and unfailing means of
constant and abundant lubrication.   The high rate of initial

speed and this automatic lubrication together obtain for the engine its great superiority over others much larger.   On the top floor of B block is the electric light dynamo.

We may interject here, by way of parenthesis, that, from the first arrival of the timber in the form of logs up to the point of the drying process, it is in charge of Mr. J. Roxburgh, who superintends its conversion into boards in the saw mill and through the drying process in block B.   He passes it over to another department, commencing with block C, which forms the " dry wood store."   Here we must, however, again cry a halt, to notice a very ingenious labour-saving contrivance which we understand to be the original conception of Mr. R. A. Shapland.   We have written of the conveyance of the wood from block B to block C.   This is how it is done : " Oblique elevators," as they may be styled, reach across the yard between the two blocks of buildings, on different grades, each conveying boards to different floors of the dry wood store.   Pairs of endless chains, driven by chain wheels, form an ever-travelling table, upon which the boards are placed at the lower end to be received on the floor upon which the higher end of the elevator is placed.   Three men are busily employed in " taking in " the incessant supply of this capable carrier.   In one-and-a-half hours, by means of the elevator, what was once the work of twenty-four hours is now accomplished.   A coal shed at the end of block C is the boundary of one side of the firm's premises.   Ere passing on to review the more intricate workmanship in which the factory excels, the admirable sanitary arrangements of the works may be mentioned.   Urinals, automatically flushed, are placed at convenient centres.

Entering block D we find that a considerable advance in

the stages of cabinet manufactures is here accomplished. Mr. Seifert, who is the foreman in this department, has a staff of twenty men under him. He is himself engaged in selecting suitable wood for the various kinds of work. Then commence the initial stages of machining. The wood is passed on to the liners, who mark it off into sizes, and indicate the destination of each portion in the piece of furniture in the manufacture of which it is to be utilised. Every piece of wood in each article of furniture, it may be explained in passing, has its number. From the liners the wood is passed on to the circular saws and cut up into the required sizes, this being preparatory to its appearance in the machine-room proper. But before we follow it, we will have a glance at a kind of saw not often seen. It is most appropriately named "the pendulum saw," a des- cription which conveys an excellent idea of its movement. While revolving, it is held by a handle attached to the spindle and moved by the operator across the board to be sawn, which is instantly severed.

The wood which is now passed down, by the lift, to the middle floor of block D, has been prepared in sets, and in this form it enters into the department which is under the superin- tendence of Mr. W. Robertson. But, whilst actually com- mencing in this middle floor of block D, the machinery department proper is in block E, to which we will proceed.

The first operation is that of "jointing up" the various pieces to the required widths. Two machines are employed upon this work. The operation accomplished, the work is passed on to the planing machines, of which there are no less than eleven of different kinds and sizes, for "flat-surfacing," "thicknessing," planing at various angles, &c. There are two high-speed mortising machines, one American and one English, and each have special attachments secured by patents.   One of the advantages peculiar to the American machine is that the chisel can be instantly reversed, whilst it is being worked at full speed, without stopping, this being done independently of the operator's hand.   A remarkable " tenoning " machine next attracts attention.   It operates on four sides of the wood at once, doing the most accurate work at a speed capable of producing 6,000 tenons per day.   In this splendidly-appointed machine-room there are also band saws employed in sawing most intricate curves ; machines for " thurming," or what is more familiarly termed " square-moulded " work, for rebating, grooving, &c.   To add to the completeness of the mechanical means of manufacture we must catalogue the presence on the same floor of three double-spindle vertical moulding-machines, for working mouldings on the edge of wide surfaces, either straight or to any irregular shape.   The machines are also used for producing shaped work of any design to a pattern on which the work is fixed.   Three similar machines, but with single vertical spindles, occupy the next floor.   It will conduce to a thorough understanding of this difference in the machines to explain that the object of the double spindles, which revolve in reverse directions, is to operate on the varying grain of the wood which runs in different directions.

The first thing which engages our attention on entering the top floor of block E, into which we are now ushered, is an automatic knife-grinder, by means of which the knives and cutters of the various planing and other machines are sharpened and kept in perfect order.   And here are also vertical and horizontal boring machines, machines for recessing, dowell-

making, &c.   Five other machines are employed in squaring
up work and cutting it to parallel sizes, and so fine is the
work done by the saws with which these are fitted that the
wood does not require to be planed afterwards.   But perhaps
the next machine bears away the palm for inventive ingenuity.
This is for dovetailing only ; another machine simultaneously
carries on the operations of dove-tailing and grooving.
Equally remarkable and interesting is its neighbour, the
purpose of which is cross dove-tailing and grooving.   Then
we have another reminder—not altogether unpleasant—of the
disaster of 1888.   The sand-papering machine, which had so
extraordinary an escape from that devastating disaster, being
saved when the fire was at its height, occupies the end of this
room.   It will be remembered that this machine was delivered
at the works on the afternoon previous to the fire, and, not
having been unpacked, was drawn out of the yard when the
Raleigh Factory had become a prey to the destructive element.
The name of the machine explains the work in which it is
employed, and it is only necessary to add that, by its oscillating and reversing action, it avoids that " lining " of the
surface of the wood which is a fault in ordinary sand-papering
machines.   A clever device for sand-papering the edges of
straight and shaped work comes next under observation.

This completes the machining department, but ere we pass
away from it the impression must be recorded that in labour-
saving appliances and the most modern mechanical aids to the
cabinet-maker's trade the factory is replete to an extent which
challenges comparison.   There is something to praise, not only
in the enterprise, practical knowledge, and keen business
aptitude of the minds that have planned the whole industry,

but in the intelligent interest which the workmen display in their occupation and the pride which they take in their admirable "tools."

Before crossing the iron bridge to block H, a visit to the ground floor of block E apprises us that one-half of it is devoted to turning lathes, square moulding and thurming cylinders, and the other half to the veneering department, which has a large and separate staff of workmen. Most interesting processes are carried on in the latter section. Pieces of figured wood are matched, joined, and manipulated, so as to produce most striking effects. Immense quantities of glue are, of course, used in this department. In the rear of the workmen are great iron presses, in which as many as twenty separate sets of veneer are laid out at the same time ; and, in contrast with these ponderous appliances, here are also seen tiniest saws at work, almost invisible in their movements ; they are employed in " letting in " and filling the various holes and defects in the veneer, and so perfectly are these inlaid that it is almost impossible to detect the piecing. Beside the fretwork saws we see at work a turning cylinder, by means of which square patterns are cut—a thing impossible in the ordinary lathe.

Block F, which it is intended to rebuild as an addition to the machine department, is not yet applied to the purpose for which it is designed. At the present moment it contains on the ground floor a great number of different kinds of sawing machines. A " flying visit " suffices for this department, therefore, and we are off again, by that rapid conveyance, the steam lift, to the top floor, from which, by way of an iron bridge, we attain block H. At the end of the bridge, another little lift

awaits us, to take us to the top floor of this building.   Here
are the stores, whence the work which has been machined is
conveyed in sets, there to be arranged, in order that they may
be given out, as required, to the cabinet makers for the operations of fitting and finishing.

That most attractive section, the carvers' department, is
situate on this floor.   Among the number of carvers employed
by the firm there are exceptionally clever craftsmen.   The
carver working in wood—the type of man working out his
destiny—imparts a romantic cast to the thought of the visitor.
He is reminded of how carvers play a part in the early literature
of England.

I contreved tooles of carpenterie, of *kerveres*,

says Langland, in " Piers Plowman," while Dryden supplies us
with the newer English :

The master painters and the *carvers* came.

And Shakespeare, whose knowledge was universal, omitted not
to employ the carver as a figure.   In Richard II., ii., 3, we have
a fine metaphor :

> I have had a feeling of my cousin's wrongs
> And laboured all I could to do him right ;
> And in the hour to come, in bearing arms,
> Be his own *carver*, and cut out his way,
> To find out right with wrong, it may not be.

Mr. William Geen has control of the craft, issuing the working
drawings from which, as the finer suites of furniture display,
some very fine carvings are produced.   Passing out of the
department we see but do not enter the ironmongery stores ;
our interest lies elsewhere.

Together, blocks H and I make a building over 200 feet

long. They are divided, in the centre of the building, by a fire-proof compartment, 12 feet in width, containing staircases which, with the landing, are made entirely of concrete on a new principle, the necessity for iron girders and the danger of their warping being avoided. Ascending to the roof of this building—from whence, by the way, we get a pretty panoramic view of the town and its surroundings—we find immense water tanks there located. They will contain many thousands of gallons of water, and are to serve as reservoirs and to supply the system of automatic sprinklers (Grinnell's patent) which has already been mentioned, as well as the ordinary pipes and hydrants which we have observed on each landing of the staircase, with hose already attached.

Another spacious lift, propelled by steam, conveys us to the floors of this building, which in both blocks (H and I) are set aside for the cabinet-makers, who here finish the work. A modern mitreing machine, most appreciated of tools, is noted in passing. The first floors of the blocks are under the respective superintendence of Messrs. M. Gabriel and C. Janes, who act as examiners of the work and pass it on to the polishing department, which is found to be on the ground floor of block H, the foreman being Mr. J. Sandell. Following the order of manufacture, we see it fitted up and finally examined in the corresponding floor of block I. Thence it goes to the packing and forwarding department, and will be loaded direct in the trucks on the railway siding about to be constructed.

In passing through the last-named departments several beautiful examples of the firm's productions are noticed, including an exceedingly handsome bedroom suite of satinwood furniture with marquetrie inlay. It would occupy considerable

space if the variety and beauty of the woods which Messrs.
Shapland & Petter utilise in their manufactures were recapitu-
lated, and as the purchasing public now have an opportunity
of viewing some of the choicer productions of the Factory at
the Cabinet Room which Mr. C. H. Godden has fitted up, with
artistic taste, on his attractive business premises at 101, High-
street, the necessity for description is obviated.

To conclude the review of these most interesting works,
we must hie to the basement of block H, which contains at one
end the veneer store and at the other end the marble-working
department.   Marble is, of course, largely employed in the
firm's manufactures, and here it is sawn and polished by
machinery.   When the basement of block I is approached a
strong ammoniacal odour excites the olfactory organs of the
visitor.   Hereby hangs a tale—another tale of means cleverly
applied to ends facilitating the course of manufacture.   The
strong "aroma" is emitted from the "fumigating" room, where
oak and mahogany goods are placed for the purpose of bringing
their hue to the required shade. The fumigating process has the
same effect upon the wood as age.   "Fumed oak" and "fumed
mahogany" are descriptive terms applied to the furniture which
has gone through this process.   This basement also contains
additional fitting rooms and stores for packing cases, etc.

From the buildings we now pass to the yard.   Outside
the workmen's entrances to block H I, a separate iron shed is
seen.   This is provided for the accommodation of oils and other
combustible materials.   Beyond this, to the railway boundary,
is the Timber and Deal yard.   The complete circuit of the
central works has now been made.   The course of our account
has shewn that the progress of the material from one depart-

o

ment to another is regular, continuous and easy, all superfluous labour being avoided. The connected plan, by which each block serves its neighbour, the raw material entering at one end (A) and appearing at the other (H I) in the form of finished furniture, has its own bearing upon the orderly arrangement of the whole extensive concern. The Raleigh Cabinet Works at present employ 300 men—designers, foremen, carvers, cabinet-makers, machinists, polishers, and labourers ; eventually their numbers will be increased.

A word of the unfinished and temporary portions of the premises. Block K is intended for showrooms and offices. Originally built as a timber shed, the fire at Raleigh necessitated that block L should be temporarily occupied as offices and workshops. At present somewhat marring the good effect produced by the other buildings, this block will eventually be made to contribute to the regularity and impressiveness of the Factory as a whole. Block G exists on paper only. Its construction has not yet been commenced, but it is probable that it will soon be in request as an auxiliary to block C for the storing of dry wood. Between block L and the railway is the Fire Brigade Depôt. The suite of offices, though temporary, are adapted to their purpose. Without enquiring how far it has affected the fortunes of the firm, the excellent advice of " Cap'n Cuttle "—" When found make a note of," suggests the transfer to our note book of this interesting motto which has a prominent place in the office : " The Secret of Success is almost always to be *before* the time "—a commercial aphorism which appeared in last year's volume of *Macmillan's Magazine.*

It remains to be said that Mr. W. C. Oliver is the architect of the Factory, and Mr. Baglow, the Foreman of the Works, ere we take our leave, turning in, on our way to the *Journal* office, to have a glimpse of some choicer specimens of the manufactures at the Raleigh works in their artistic setting at the Cabinet Room in the rear of Mr. C. H. Godden's fine china show-room, at 101, High Street. The show-room and its choice contents enhance the impression that, in this series of articles we have reserved the " best wine " till the last.

XVI.—WEAR GIFFORD FLOUR MILL.

No one will be found to cavil at the resumption of this series of articles with a description of a modern flour mill. Yeo, Taw and Torridge—the trio of rivers that swell the volume of the Severn sea—turn many a merry mill that grinds the flour to make the daily bread of the inhabitants of North Devon. And millers there are galore, full as jolly as he, famed in song, who lived by the river Dee. So that, in pursuing the practice which has been observed in our industrial papers, of selecting a representative example of an industry flourishing in the district in which the *Journal* circulates, we are but doing justice to a feature of our commerce which merits consideration. " And why Wear Gifford Mill ? " asks the man of the Metropolis of North Devon. For the very simple reason that here, without doubt, is now existant the most modern milling machinery of which the world wots. " Infinite riches in a little room " was a fine compliment paid by a courtier ; and it is but a plain statement of fact to say that Mr. Thomas Fry has, with signal enterprise, placed Wear Gifford mill on a pinnacle of mechanical perfection which will cause the millwright, whoever he may be, to unhesitatingly class it " A 1." The artist and

o 2

the lover of rural sights and sounds may sigh over the departure of "the mill by the rivulet" which "evermore sounds, clip ! clap !! clip ! clap !! " but in this utilitarian age beauty largely lies in use ; and the visitor to this mechanically admirably appointed mill, lit by electricity, and turning out flour that challenges comparison in purity, will not be slow in expressing his admiration for the revolution which skill and enterprise has brought about.

The mill is on the weir which undoubtedly gave its name to the pretty land-locked village where the Torridge flashes o'er its pebbly bed through the lea.   Hills rise on every hand, sheltering the secluded valley.   Wear wood is in the rear of the mill and Southcott wood on its left.   The charming surroundings of the mill, the Weir itself and the quaint bridge where feudalism—in the form of a half-penny toll—still lingers ; leave the ruraliser little room for protestation against the depletion of familiar country sights and sounds, such as the moss-covered mill and the musical monotone with which it accompanies its mission to a million mouths.

Wear Gifford might have " sat " for the " happy valley " of Johnson's " Rasselas." The picturesque village, with its fine parish church, and famous hall, the carved oak of which has a Devonian reputation ; the strawberry gardens (with which the Cockney taste inevitably and instinctively associates the " clotted cream " of luscious memory), and the quaint straggling street of the hamlet, all shut in by the circling hills, proclaim a placid little world "far from the madding crowd."

The Fry family have been associated with Wear Gifford Mill for over a century.   The great grandfather (Mr. Samuel

Plate 25 (above) Vaughan's Glove Factory about 1900. Note the hand operated screw presses; *26 below)* Vaughan's Glove Factory, Torrington

Plate 27 (above) Shapland & Petters' New Raleigh Cabinet Works, from a drawing dated 1904; *28 (below)* Weare Gifford Flour Mill about 1888 with the river Torridge in flood. Note the line of the original roof on the end wall, and also one of the large cast-iron gear wheels leaning against the wall

Fry) and the grandfather of the present proprietor, Mr. Thomas
Fry, held it for a number of years ; his widow carried it on for
a term ; then it came into the hands of Mr. John Fry, passing
to his son some seventeen years since.   The era of alteration
and improvement began with the advent of the present owner,
who has finally resolved upon, and carried out on a compre-
hensive scale, the thorough modernising of the mill.   Among
other "old things" which have passed away on the advent of
new inventions, is that most important part of this occupation
which, according to Yarrell, in his erudite work on " British
Fishes," in its exercise, by a peculiar and constant action of
the muscles, smoothed, broadened and rounded the thumb of
a miller in such a way as to cause the head of that ugly
little fish, the "miller's thumb," to be compared to it.   In
this way we lose the etymology of the bywords of many generations.

Exterior alterations naturally attract the earliest attention
of the visitor, and the old mill wheel being conspicuous by its
absence, he is naturally interested in solving the problem as to
the water motor endowed with the power to drive the accumu-
lated machinery. The cross-boards of the old mill-wheel remain
as relics of the former state, but the new motor is invisible.
A dam has been built up, in the shape of a stone-walled tank,
where the wheel stood, and in the depth of water thus obtained
a 30-inch Victor Turbine water-wheel runs its rapid revolutions.
The great advantage of this remarkable piece of milling
machinery is the extraordinary power which it develops in
proportion to its diameter.   Economy of space, great speed,
light gearing, less wear and tear and loss in transmitting power
are further excellences which commend its use in the propulsion

of machinery. Scientific tests by competent and disinterested engineers have led to the Victor Turbine establishing the "best on record " for power and efficiency, and the results developed. The maximum horse power of the 30-inch wheel, when employed for ordinary purposes, is 52·54, whilst the per centage of useful effect attained by it is ·8676. These great results, however, would necessitate that it should be working from an head of twelve feet. At Wear Gifford Mill an head of eight feet has been obtained ; the wheel makes 91 revolutions per minute, using 2,346 cubic feet of water in this brief period of time, and attaining 30·10 horse power. This enormous capacity in a small diameter and high per centage of useful effect is obtained by simple, strong construction and a perfect gate. The visitor looks into the wheel-pit and sees a slight commotion in the water, but otherwise the powerful turbine proceeds noiselessly with its work.   The vertical wheel revolves within an iron case, receives the water upon the outside and discharges it downward and outward, the splash and the dash with which the water enters the tail-race from the wheel-pit indicating the high revolving speed of the wheel. Entering the flume or tank from the head-race of the weir, the water makes its way through the fixed water-ways of the duplex chute, formed by the outer chute case and the inside register gate, which regulates the supply of water to the wheel that revolves within it.   From the flume the water is discharged into the tail-race, where it dashes on, with acccumulated speed, to join the brimming river. The sight of the swirling stream reminds us of the passage in Shakespeare's little read " Titus Andronicus : "

"More water glideth by the mill,
Than wots the miller of."

The motive power is communicated to the shafting in the customary way. The main drive has a double 8-inch belt, and propels what is practically the whole of the machinery of the automatic roller plant. A second pulley of smaller dimensions drives the dynamo of the system of electric lighting which is not the least striking novelty in this country mill. The barley mill is set in motion by a third pinion, the three pulleys being on the same shaft. Mr. Frederick Nell, of Mark Lane, London, is the patentee and manufacturer of the Victor Turbine.

From the motor the mill itself is the natural sequence. Its exterior indicates recent alteration, the mill having been carried a storey higher by an ingenious arrangement which lost not a slate off the roof of the building. It is a compact, oblong structure, with little space wasted on superfluities. The milling expert is still on the premises, and the electrician is busy with his accumulators. Our " watchword " in noticing our local industries has been " begin at the beginning," and in order to do this we have to ascend, leaving the electric light for our last consideration.

Mr. Henry Simon, of Manchester, now commands a world-wide reputation as the manufacturer of automatic roller plant for milling purposes which challenges comparison in efficiency. Under the supervision of Mr. Kitson, one of Mr. Simon's smart engineers, plant has been erected at Wear Gifford Mill which embodies the very latest advances in milling machinery. The more modern equipments of the pre-existing mill have been utilized, but, to all intents and purposes, Mr. Fry has thoroughly reorganised his undertaking and placed it in the forefront of milling industries, mechanically considered.

The Torridge is navigable near to the mill, and barges
bring up the imported corn upon the top of the tide, while
local supplies are carted to the mill.   An ingenious hoist lands
the sacks at the top of the mill, where they are stacked,
previous to the operation of mixing.   Deep bins with hopper
bottoms have been built into the frame of the mill, the outlet
from these centreing in the mixing-room, where the handling
of wheat goes on with ease and facility, a worm conveyor
taking the mixed wheat on to the elevators, where the process
of cleaning begins.   We will follow the wheat from the hoist
to the stacking, thence in its drop to the hutches, next to the
mixing room, and now to the "Eureka" Brush Finishing
Machine, of Howes and Ewell, where it is effectually cleaned.
The removal of the dirt from the wheat involves a series of
operations.   The "Eureka Zigzag" separator, the eccentric
action of which is admirably defined in its name, first separates
and sifts away all deleterious matter.   Then the "Eureka
Scourer" justifies *its* name, the Brush Finishing Machine completing the cleaning, and a fan blows away the dust and refuse
—the snow-like cloud of husks whose shower falls on the bank
of the mill stream strongly distinguishing the "clean wheat"
of the farmer from the article which has passed through this
effective purifying process.   Elevated again, now to the brush
machine, the wheat is subjected to a cleansing which leaves
no impurity behind, and then enters the clean wheat-bin, on
the top or fourth floor of the mill.

The roller mill of Simon's splendid manufacture now takes
the grain in hand.   The well-known Manchester roller mills
for "breaking" wheat on the system of five breaks and
"flouring" the middlings and semolina in eight reductions

have been adopted by Mr. Fry in their entirety. The " breaking " of the wheat is the introductory operation. For the purpose of the " first break " the wheat is conveyed to the second floor, where it is effected with four grooved chilled iron rollers. The mechanism of these rollers—the ingenious arrangements by which the operation is started, stopped and regulated, defy description, but impress the visitor with the clock-work perfection to which milling machinery has been brought. From the first break, the wheat is elevated to the third floor, where it passes to a double rotary scalper (the millwrights don't consult one's feelings ; they call a spade a spade) ; this machine does the work of three. In the first place it separates the fine and the coarse grain, despatching the latter to the second break, from whence it returns to the scalper again. The principle of the scalper is that it receives the fine flour, which passes through its seive, sending it on to the " silk reel " to be dressed, whilst the coarse is returned to the succession of breaks, and is subjected to further reductions. With the " automatic feed " the " breaks " can be adjusted to regulate the fineness of the material to whatever shade the miller requires. The cleaned and polished wheat, in passing through these four sets of fluted (corrugated) iron rolls, which effects the " breaks " and reductions, is freed from the kernel, while the bran is cleansed. The " rotary scalper," as has been shown, has three distinct departments. The fine material is sent by it to one shoot, the remainder being returned to the second, third and fourth " breaks," to be broken and " reduced " again. The fine must now be followed to the reel, whence it is conveyed by the elevator. The reel is a long octagonal cylinder covered with silk, and its purpose is that of a separator. " Flour," " middlings," and " semolina " have entered the " reel " together. The finished flour is separated and falls to the collecting worm, which conveys it to the shoot on the way to be sacked. But the two after products, middlings and semolina, have yet to pass through an exceedingly interesting series of dressing processes. They are, in the course of the elaborate operations of the double reform purifier, dusted and graded into different sizes, and passed to purifiers, where all light and injurious matter is removed. The pure material which then remains is conducted to five sets of smooth iron rolls, where it is finally pulverised. In the final effective purifying operation, it enters the octagonal centrifugal cylinder, which is covered with fine silk, and completes the dressing process. It has beaters like fan blades, revolving six or eight times faster than the cylinder itself. Entering at the spout, the finished flour drops to the collecting worm from three-fourths of the revolving cylinder, the " cut-off " portion, a fourth of the whole cylinder, returning part of the flour to the final roll, which effects the last reduction. The collecting worms run at right angles to the centrifugal cylinder, and the flour is thus conveyed to the shoots, whence it falls into the sacks. The three final products are flour, fine offal, and bran. It is needless to say that the flour, after these various efficient operations, is purity itself. In the operation of extracting the wheat from its branny covering and converting it into flour, it has passed nine times through the roller mills, and if we add the cleansing processes, there are a round dozen of distinct operations, all directed to the essential object of producing flour of absolute purity.

By the old process, in which the flour was ground between

the upper and nether mill-stone, the nature of the flour was destroyed ; the product of the roller mills,—which has gone through the process of gradual separation of the floury from the branny matter of the wheat, as opposed to the old stoning method, which accomplished this is one operation, and in doing so inevitably absorbed impure material in the flour,—retains the nature of the wheat, in its velvety, granular character. In grinding the grain with stones the germ flakes were not removed ; hence it happened that flour was open to the danger of turning rancid, in consequence of the presence of the germ, which is of an oily nature. The distributed operations of the roller mill permit of the removal of the germ flake by the centrifugal operation which follows each " reduction." The germ, thus separated, is excellent food for horses, sheep and pigs.

The system of worm conveyors and elevators, by means of which the grain is distributed and carried forward through the different operations, and the flour collected and carried to the sack's mouth, is most elaborate and efficient. It is by these means that operations so various in character are carried on within the confines of the mill. The wood-work of the elevators, as well as the shafting of the entire machinery, is of a most workman-like description, and contributes to the impressive effect which the efficiency of the whole process of roller-milling makes upon the mind of the visitor. The compact character of the mill as a whole is its distinguishing characteristic. Messrs. Garnish and Lemon, of Pilton, Barnstaple, fitted the machinery.

On the ground floor of the mill we see the shoots bringing the flour from the final operations in the storey above, sacks being filled at their mouths and set aside awaiting the miller's waggon and his fine team of draught horses. The steady, effulgent electric light with which the floor is lit reminds us that we have yet to investigate a striking new departure on the part of a West country miller.

Needless to say the advent of the electric light in Wear Gifford is a source of wonder to the rural population, who find a serious obstacle to the easy tracing of " cause and effect." The light is there, and very brilliant it is ! But where does it come from ? " *Where's the oil ?* " as the not unreasonable domestic enquired, for the connection between the oil in the lamp and the burning wick is clear. To the most cultured mind a simple definition of what electricity is would present a greater difficulty than a problem in Euclid or a Greek *jeu d'ésprit* in the original. If Wear Gifford looks upon the electric light as a mystery akin to the wonderful lamp of Aladdin, there is nothing surprising in the fact.

Mr. Fry has adopted Robotham's system, the installation being effected by Mr. Fox, in the employ of the patenting firm. The advantage claimed for the system is that it is run with one switch, charging and discharging. With a maximum capacity of 55 lights, the normal use will be 38 lights. The newest type of machine is employed, An ordinary drum-wound dynamo ; the Electric Power Company's (E. P. C.) storage cells ; and Edison's Swan lamps, are the first-class features. The motor power is, of course, supplied by the turbine. The machine gives an output of 50 volts. It is fitted with the patent acme switch and Dorman and Smith's fuse. The mill is lighted with 13 lamps, the remainder being distributed between the gate, yard, stables, and residence of

Mr. Fry. The pleasantly-situate dwelling-house is lit throughout in a most efficient manner.

Mr. Fry's enterprise is thus extended beyond the confines of his business, and as a pioneer of electric lighting in rural North Devon he has gained a very honourable distinction. The peculiar facilities he possesses for availing himself of the highest scientific product of nineteenth century civilisation, of course, suggested the installation, but here, and in the projected addition of a telephone connecting his residence and the mill, the same enterprise and commercial acumen is seen which has manifested itself in the creation, at Wear Gifford Mill, of an industry boasting the attainment of the van of mechanical perfection in an age prolific in invention. Lit by electricity, possessing a water motor of exceptional power, and a plant in describing which the term excellent may be employed with its fullest significance, we shall have to search the United Kingdom through ere we find a country mill so splendidly equipped as the valuable property of Mr. Fry at pretty Wear Gifford.

XVII.—THE EXE VALLEY FISH-BREEDING ESTABLISHMENT.

As old as the hills themselves is the art of pisciculture. Isaiah, foreshadowing the confusion of Egypt (Isaiah xix, 10), prophesied, " And they shall be broken in the purposes thereof, *all that make sluices and ponds for fish.*" That the pleasant pastime of fishing was not neglected by the ancients is clear from the numerous allusions in classic literature to the sport.

> Smoothly flow the watery stores
> Of *fishy* Hipparis, profoundest stream,

West makes Pindar say in his version of the fifth " Olympiad."

Fishponds were made where former forests grew,

sings Prior in his *Solomon*. If we take good Izaak Walton as
an authority on the preservation of the sport of "quiet men,
and followers of peace," such as anglers are, he will tell us that
it is " as ancient as Deucalion's flood," and that Belus, " who
was the first inventor of godly and virtuous recreations," neglected little provision that the sport which Seth, one of the
sons of Adam, taught his offspring, should not lack for want of
fish. Fish -culture was, however, slow in assuming its present
proportions, and it is in America that it chiefly flourishes
to-day. John Shaw, gamekeeper to the Duke of Buccleuch, is
credited with the revival of the art in Britain, about 1837; and
to " Shaw of Drumlanrig" are even now attributed certain
original discoveries. In the course of ichthyological inves-
tigations, he had occasion to fecundate the eggs of salmon and
rear the young. Five years later an illiterate French fisherman
named Remy began the culture of trout at Vosges, in France.
But the first known breeding station or " piscifactory " was
established, in 1850, at Hünnigen, in Alsace, by the French
Government. King Leopold, following suit, carried on successful experiments in the breeding of trout, near his new palace
of Ardennes. And to-day, whilst we possess a National Fish
Culture Association in England, the American Government
appear to be most alive to the importance of the art.

Are our rivers being depopulated of the finny tribe? The
question is by no means untimely or unfounded. A river may
quickly be emptied of its anadromous visitors by over fishing
in the spawning season as well as by dams which cut off the
fish from their spawning grounds. Wonderful stories are told

of the leap of salmon over seemingly impassable barriers in their eagerness to get into shallow water, in which the ova is deposited where it may have the genial influence of the sun's rays. But in our Devonshire rivers, as elsewhere, dams have been constructed of such a height and nature as to be effective obstructions to the passing of the fish to and from their spawning ground. In and in breeding has its deleterious effects. Without any introduction of fresh blood, degeneration cannot but ensue. Whether or not this is the cause, or that our rivers have been (as they may be) over fished to such a degree that angling has become anything but a pleasure, it is the opinion of many " old stagers " among the followers of the gentle craft that there has been an appreciable decadence in the quantity and quality of fish taken in our fresh-water rivers. Mr. Francis Langdon, the proprietor of the Exe Valley Fish-breeding Establishment, is firmly of this opinion. His belief is based upon an intimate acquaintance with sport on the rivers of Devon and Somerset during the past thirty years. From early youth up he has been what, without any ill reflection, we may style an inveterate angler, and it is his strong conviction that it is only by fresh stocking the streams that the craft can hope to enjoy a long lease of their favourite recreation. This, he thinks, they will be quite prepared to do, once the alternative is put before them of losing their sport or securing its maintenance by a slight general contribution to a fund originated for this express purpose. It would be nothing short of a deprivation to the disciples of the amiable, garrulous Izaak, if the day should come when it would be said of our streams, as Tom Hughes writes in *Tom Brown at Oxford*: " There was only a small piece of *fishable* water at Englebourne." **Far** preferable would it be if we might continue to boast of our county, with Camden in his *Remains*, that it is " watered with pleasant *fishful* rivers."

Mr. Langdon has shown his interest in the subject in a very practical way. The great object of fish culture is to aid in maintaining a natural supply, to repair the effects of past improvidence, and to increase the supply beyond its natural limits, in order that emergencies may be met. That enterprise which has for years manifested itself in the possession and breeding of pedigree-stock, in regard to which Mr. Langdon, whose name appears in the Herd Book, is held to be an authority, two years since was extended in the direction of pisciculture. Where the Exe and the Barle effect their junction, as Blackmore describes in his charming romance, *Lorna Doone*, this enthusiastic fisherman has expended some £500 in laying out " sluices and ponds for fish," it may be very much after the pattern of those upon which the Egyptian Pharaohs lavished the wealth won to them by their myriad slaves. The traveller on the Devon and Somerset railway, as he leaves Dulverton, the popular centre of a famous hunting country, may, as he shoots over the bridge that crosses the Exe, have his attention arrested by a novel arrangement of a series of ponds in the lea leading down to a new building, beyond which there are three ponds more of different shape. This is, as yet, the modest extent of the Exe Valley Fish-breeding Establishment, but pisciculturists who have already visited the new breeding station have been surprised at its size and efficiency. In a circular which he has issued " to all whom it may concern," Mr. Langdon draws public attention to the necessity for the re-stocking of rivers, ponds, lakes, &c., with trout

(Salmo fario). He has found, on the inspection of various rivers, that the trout have degenerated, owing to the want of fresh blood, and on this ground he has started an Hatchery under his own supervision, with the assistance of a man of many years' experience, and has been successful in securing large parent trout from different rivers (some from a long distance) at considerable cost. With caution, he has managed to cross them, so as to produce very strong offspring, and he is confident that the young fish will do well in any waters in which they may be placed.

We do not yet appear to have attained to the ingenuity of the Chinese, who hatch fry under fowls, emptying a hen's egg and its natural contents and substituting the spawn for it, when the aperture is closed and the egg put under its natural parent, being removed and re-opened in a few days, then placed in a vessel of water warmed by the heat of the sun, where it is kept till the young fish are developed. The fertilisation of the fresh egg, as practised by the British pisciculturist, is a simple process. It is done by pressing the ripe ova from the female fish into a shallow receptacle and then squeezing out the milt of the male over them. The heavy non-adhesive eggs of the trout, whose specific gravity is so great that they will not float, are placed in thin layers upon the bottoms of perforated zinc trays, through which a current of water is constantly passing. In breeding common trout this course is sometimes taken : An oblong box is found and the bottom filled with clean, good gravel, crushed small. In the month of November, a few weeks before spawning, a spawner and a milter of good size are placed in a box, which is then sunk in a deep stream, where there is plenty of water. When the fish

P

have cast, they are turned adrift into the river, and the box is
moved into shallow water, which, with a temperature raised
by the rays of the sun, brings forth the fry in due season.
They are kept in the box until they are about half-an-inch
long, then turned out on the shallows.

But in the system adopted by Mr. Langdon an hatchery
and rearing ponds are substituted for the stream itself, and the
processes of hatching and rearing go on under the immediate
supervision of the keeper and the proprietor of the establishment. Ten trays with sectional boxes are arranged on half as
many tables on one side of the oblong chamber, into which the
sun penetrates through skylights. Over each tray is a water
tap, and beneath it an outlet ; and there is a constant supply
of fresh water both to the ova and the fish. The " gay
deceiver " of months is not the time for seeing fish-breeding in
full swing, but we are brought acquainted with its most interesting features. In one of the small compartments formed by
little trays of perforated zinc floating in the bigger tray, we
find the ova itself. Round at first, it assumes a variety of
shapes ere the fry are hatched. Here are a few of the new-
born trout, with the umbilical sac still attached to their
bellies. They will receive their sustenance from the sac for
forty days. This year sixty-five days have sufficed for hatching. This is an abnormally short period, as the average is
eighty-four days. The mildness of the winter may have contributed to the early appearance of the new generation of the
finny tribe.

In another section a lively fraternity of fish which have
cast off the sign of dependence contained in the sac and disport
themselves freely, exhibiting their prettily striped bodies as

they glide up the side of the tray, are fed with grated liver. They are dainty folk, and have a delicate appetite. No epicurean could be more choice in his selection of viands than Master Trout, who "refuses" this and that "dish" until he has met a tit-bit to his liking, which he voraciously consumes. With the invitation to the feast,

> Let good digestion wait on appetite,
> And health on both,

we pass on to observe the "cripples" (as they are known to the keeper) who are the objects of pity. The greatly-deformed trout has but a fleeting existence, but every experienced angler has probably met with a monstrosity which has lived to maturity. Here are fry with two heads and one tail; one which can only get along on its belly; another afflicted with that common upward curvature of the spine, a little behind the head, which makes the fish appear in some degree humpbacked; a fourth lies curled up like a snail; others have crooked tails, and one has a prominent under jaw. But the "phenomena" are few in number when compared with "the lusty trout," prettily marked and finely made, which are here in their thousands. When they have attained the dignity of yearlings, the fish are ready for exportation. Trout are supplied from the establishment during the months of November, December, January, February, March, and April. The demand has been so great in Mr. Langdon's case that he has been reluctantly compelled to get orders cancelled.

Leaving the Hatchery—over which lives the keeper, William Ballinger, from Northampton, who recently succeeded Nathan Woodruffe Ashton, of Hope, Yorkshire, who was associated with the National Fish Culture Association, and whose

P 2

death, from heart disease, was regretted by pisciculturists—
we make our way to the rearing ponds. The door of the
Hatchery is widespread, that the fry may have all the air
possible.

The rearing-ponds are six in number. They are divided by
perforated sluices, and there is a continuous fresh supply of
water from the Barle. Out in the meadow our surroundings
are charming. Away to the North West stretch the gorse-
clad hills of Exmoor with Dunkerry Beacon towering high o'er
all, and the valleys of the Barle and the Exe. "West by
North," still further, is the new coach route between Dulverton
and Lynton, organised by Mr. Nelder, of the Carnarvon Arms,
Dulverton, and Mr. Bevan, of the Lynton Hotel, with the
prestige of the Great Western Railway Company at their
back. A charming route, indeed, which takes the tourist over
Exmoor, and, from the haunts of the wild red deer, descends to
the vale of Lyn—twenty-six miles of such scenery as only the
West of England can attract the traveller with. Just below us
is Exbridge, "a name to all the country dear," whilst south-
ward lies Tiverton. We are at the fork of the two rivers, and
the "scientific frontier" of the counties lies within a few yards
of us. The shrill whistle of the train warns us of the approach
of the Devon and Somerset "express," and immediately the
little group by the rearing ponds is the cynosure of all eyes for
a second, as the swift messenger of modern invention flashes by.
Lest it may appear that our geography is somewhat at fault
in counting a "piscifactory" in the Exe Valley among the
industries of North Devon, we may again quote the circular
of the proprietor, in which he writes from "Exbridge, Tiverton,
Devon."

Plate 29 The carding machine once used in the Turton blanket factory at Weare Gifford. It had been converted for reflocking mattresses

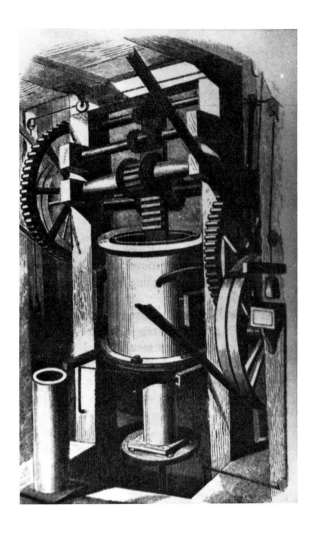

Plate 30 Drain-pipe making machine similar to those used in the local potteries and brickyard

To return to our fish, with which the process of rearing, like Tennyson's brook, knowing no interruption, has gone on during our digression, we note that each pond is fifteen yards long, by three-and-a-half wide. At the present moment there are two-and-a-half feet of water, another foot being added when the stream runs in at its full force. But the ponds contain small fish just now, and as the wind is tempered to the shorn lamb on the uplands that form an extensive part of the farm of Mr. Langdon, some five or six hundred acres in extent, so the little fish and their susceptibilities are considered. The fish are draughted from one to the other of the six ponds as they grow, for the very excellent reason that if this were not done they would eat each other, and the principle of the survival of the fittest would have a crude application. If it were a profitable argument, we might proceed to consider how far the nature of the fish of "cannibal" propensities is affected by what it eats in this unorthodox way. As an instance of the influence of what he eats upon the nature of man a humorous contemporary has put forward a cannibal turned missionary. The *Salmo fario* have enemies enough and to spare outside their own ranks to excuse them from preying upon one another. How perennially true is the famous epigram—

> Big fleas have little fleas upon their backs, to bite 'em,
> And little fleas have lesser fleas, and so *ad infinitum!*

From yonder oak tree, whose acorns will fall in the centre of the ponds, a gay-plumaged kingfisher will keep a keen eye upon the rearing-trout, and dart down from his coign of vantage to snatch an unlucky yearling from the placid life of the pond. The otter, who has a tooth for trout, may take the ponds in the course of his peregrinations. And these snare-lines that stretch across the pond and are connected with Burgess's patent alarm guns, apprise us that a warm reception is prepared for fishers yet more destructive than he of the long beak, the tufted crest, and the fine feathers. Be it said to the honour of old Devon, however, no one has yet poached upon Mr. Langdon's "preserves." When the summer comes, Mr. Langdon will protect the ponds with netting.

In the upper pond are a fine lot of yearlings for breeding purposes. A cautious observer may find them, in season, making their homes under the banks, and it is a pretty sight to come upon them feeding in the sunshine. The bigger fish are fed on boiled horseflesh, which is reduced to large and small worm-like pieces in a meat chopper, the sizes being suited to the age of the fishes. Mr. Langdon will not breed from his fish until they are three years old. Spawn should not be continuously taken from the same fish. It is sometimes complained of the Exe and Barle fish that they are of a small variety. Among the fish which Mr. Langdon has purchased for crossing purposes are bigger fish from different waters. The Tone, the Otter, the Stour, and the Kennet (Wiltshire) are represented in the varieties which he now possesses. Crossing the home trout with the imported *Salmo fario*, he obtains a variety possessed of the good qualities of both. Mr. Langdon has offered to get down salmon ova from the Severn waters for the Exe, and it is to be hoped the authorities will avail themselves of his generosity.

The sluice which admits the water that continuously flows through the perforated hatchways of the rearing ponds serves another purpose. Ere the fish are sent away they are put in the dam where the rushing water is in full play upon them.

From the fact that fresh-water fish have a liking for the neighbourhood of agitated water, and circle about the hatch-ways where the water is in commotion, it is not a vain supposition which assumes that they enjoy this change. At any rate they come out as clean as possible, and are far from being sickly when they are sent away. These rearing ponds, on the banks of the Barle, almost answer to the old fish-garths—staked or dammed enclosures on the margin of a river to form a fish preserve. The old fishing " cruive " was another pisci-cultural device, being an enclosure for fish in a river.

We have yet to visit the stock ponds, three in number, which lie below the Hatchery, nearer Exbridge. These are fed from the mill-stream, the supply of fresh water being continuous here also. Each pond is let out separately by an ingenious arrangement which is the original device of Mr. Langdon. Draughting from the ponds commences in the last week of October. The male and female fish have each a separate pond, the third being reserved for imported trout, mixed male and female. Each is between six and seven feet deep, and contains large quantities of *Salmo fario.* To prevent the trout from making the inlets and outlets from the ponds of the nature of fish-ways, which are devices to enable the finny tribe to ascend a fall, the pipe-ends are covered with perforated zinc. The frisky fish would otherwise take a leap into the pipe's mouth, and, with their propensity for swimming against stream, quickly be off in search of adventure.

It is rather interesting to see the trout in transport. This was permitted us the other day when a consignment of year-lings from the Exe Valley Fish-breeding Establishment were on their way to Watermouth Castle. The fish were contained in a barrel, after the nature of a brewer's. In place of the bung-hole was a piece of perforated zinc, and when the train in which the consignment was being conveyed stopped, the keeper had a pair of bellows in requisition with which he kept up a constant supply of air to the fish. When the train is in motion the natural supply is sufficient. Beside Mr. Basset, the following have received large supplies of fish from the Exe Valley establishment during the two years of its existence : Messrs. Hansard & Son, of London, for stocking the Wiley, at Wilton, near Salisbury ; Major Barrett, Morebath ; Mr. Thompson, Taunton, and the Conservators and riparian owners of other rivers. Yearlings are sent in large canisters with perforated necks, enclosed in wicker-work.

Although Mr. Langdon, as yet, confines his enterprise in fish-breeding to the *Salmo fario*, his services are occasionally in demand in obtaining salmon for stocking purposes. Just now the young salmon in the Barle have got their beautiful silver coat—they have remained over the second winter in the home waters, but now, issuing from the parr stage, they have assumed their migratory dress and are prepared to go to sea. Their " coming of age " is marked by their investment with the transverse dusky bars and bright spots which are the " escutcheon " of the smelt. In this stage they are available for transport to other rivers. Mr. Langdon possesses fishing rights with his farm, a large portion of which he rents from the Earl of Carnarvon, the lord of the manor.

Discarding even the legal cunning gibbeted in the couplet :

> While others fish with craft for great opinion,
> I with great truth catch mere simplicity,

there may still be found throughout the borders of North

Devon numbers of those of whom genial, honest Walton wrote
"they love the art of angling." For them the preservation of
the "pleasant pastime" will be a source of concern, and, hence,
they will adjudge that an industry dedicated to this purpose is
eminently entitled to rank among the most interesting and
worthy of the "factories" of North Devon. If we may be
permitted to add to the weighty words of sententious Markham, in his "Country Contentments," we would say that there
is something wanting beside "proper habits, good tackle in
his pannier, and so much science in his head," ere "our angler
would stand a pretty good chance to catch fish." Says Markham, after his quaint fashion, "these are little to the purpose
without the Christian virtues of faith, hope, and charity; and
unless two at least of the cardinal virtues can be persuaded to
go a-fishing, the angler may as well stay at home." Yet,
again, wise and virtuous Markham, it were necessary that
there should be fish to be caught. The Romans, in the height
of their glory, made fish the mistress of all their entertain-
ments, quoth Izaak Walton, and "He that shall view the
writings of Macrobius, or Varro, may be confirmed and informed of this, and of the incredible value of their fish and
fish-ponds." Englishmen have arisen to the fact that, for
commerce and for pleasure, they have in their fisheries a
property worthy their careful consideration. The existence of
the National Fish Culture Association is an outward and
visible symbol of this interest, and at the Exe Valley Fish-
breeding Establishment we see what the individual enterprise
of an enthusiastic angler is doing for the craft.

INDEX